MACMILLAN LITERATURE COLLECTIONS

Love Stories

edited by Lesley Thompson

Published by Macmillan Education
Between Towns Road, Oxford OX4 3PP
A division of Macmillan Publishers Limited
Companies and representatives throughout the world

ISBN 978–0–2307–1692–6

All additional material written by Lesley Thompson

First published 2009
Text © Macmillan Publishers Limited 2009
Design and illustration © Macmillan Publishers Limited 2009
This version first published 2009

The authors and publishers are grateful for permission to reprint the
following copyright material:

A P Watts Limited for the story 'The Jilting of Jane' by H. G. Wells.
Reproduced with permission of A P Watts on behalf of The Literary
Executors of the Estate of H G Wells;

David Higham Associates Limited for the stories 'The Sensible Thing' from
The Collected Short Stories of F Scott Fitzgerald by F Scott Fitzgerald; and
'A Shocking Accident' from Collected Short Stories by Graham Greene.
Reproduced with permission of David Higham Associates;

Pollinger Limited for the story 'A Christmas Song' by H E Bates.
Reproduced by permission of pollinger Limited and the Estate of H E Bates;

These materials may contain links for third party websites. We have no
control over, and are not responsible for, the contents of such third party
websites. Please use care when accessing them.

Cover by Corbis/LWA-Stephen Welstead & Getty/Nacivet

Printed and bound in Thailand

2011   2010   2009
6   5   4   3   2

Contents

Macmillan Literature Collections

Welcome to the *Macmillan Literature Collections* – a series of advanced-level readers containing original, unsimplified short stories written by famous classic and modern writers. We hope that these stories will help to ease your students' transition from graded readers to reading authentic novels.

Each collection in the series includes:

Introduction

- an introduction to the short story
- tips for reading authentic texts in English
- an introduction to the genre
- a carefully-chosen selection of classic and modern short stories.

The stories

Each story is presented in three parts: the introduction and pre-reading support material; the story; and post-reading activities. Each part includes the following sections:

- *About the author* – in-depth information about the author and their work
- *About the story* – information about the story, including background information about setting and cultural references
- *Summary* – a brief summary of the story that does not give away the ending.

Pre-reading exercises

- *Key vocabulary* – a chance to look at some of the more difficult vocabulary related to the main themes and style of the story before reading the story
- *Main themes* – a brief discussion of the main themes, with questions to keep in mind as you read.

The story

You will find numbered footnotes in the stories. These explain cultural and historical references, and key words that you will need to understand the text. Many of these footnotes give definitions of words which are very formal, old-fashioned or rarely used in modern English. You will find more common, useful words and phrases from the stories in the *Glossary* at the end of the book. Words included in the *Glossary* will appear in **bold**.

Post-reading exercises

- *Understanding the story* – comprehension questions that will help you make sure you've understood the story
- *Language study* – a section that presents and practises key linguistic and structural features of authentic literary texts (you will find an index of the areas covered at the end of the book)
- *Literary analysis* – discussion questions that guide you to an in-depth appreciation of the story, its structure, its characters and its style.

In addition, at the end of each book there are:
- suggested *Essay questions*
- a comprehensive *Glossary* highlighting useful vocabulary from each story
- an **index** for the *Language study* section.

How to use these books

You can use these books in whatever way you want. You may want to start from the beginning and work your way through. You may want to pick and choose. The *Contents* page gives a very brief, one-line introduction to each story to help you decide where to start. You may want to learn about the author and the story before you read each one, or you may prefer to read the story first and then find out more about it afterwards. Remember that the stories and exercises can be challenging, so you may want to spend quite a long time studying each one. The most important thing is to enjoy the collection – to enjoy reading, to enjoy the stories and to enjoy the language that has been used to create them.

—

Answer keys

In many cases you can check your answers in the story by using the page references given. However, an Answer key for all the exercises will be available on the student's section of the Macmillan Readers website at www.macmillanenglish.com/readers

Introduction

What is a short story?

A short story is shorter than a novel, but longer than a poem. It is usually between 1,000 and 20,000 words long. It tells a story which can usually be read quite quickly. It often concentrates on one, central event; it has a limited number of characters, and takes place within a short space of time.

History of the short story

Stories and storytelling have existed for as long as people have had language. People love, and need, stories. They help us explain and understand the world. Before people could read or write, storytellers travelled from village to village, telling stories.

The first written stories developed from this storytelling tradition. Two of the best-known examples of early, written stories in Europe appeared in the 14th century. Chaucer's *Canterbury Tales* and Bocaccio's *Decameron* are both based on the same idea – a group of people who are travelling or living together for a short time, agree to tell each other stories.

The first modern short stories appeared at the beginning of the 19th century. Early examples of short-story collections include the *Fairy Tales* (1824–26) of the Brothers Grimm, and Edgar Allan Poe's *Tales of the Grotesque and Arabesque* (1840). In the late 19th century, printed magazines and journals became very popular and more and more short stories were published. By the 20th century most well-known magazines included short stories in every issue and the publishers paid a lot of money for them. In 1952 Ernest Hemingway's short story, *The Old Man and the Sea*, helped sell more than five million copies of the magazine *Life* in just two days.

The short story today

Today, short stories are often published in collections called anthologies. They are usually grouped according to a particular category – by theme, topic, national origin, time, or author. Some newspapers and magazines continue to print individual stories. Many short stories are first published on the Internet, with authors posting them on special-interest websites and in online magazines.

Reading authentic literary texts in English

Reading authentic literary texts can be difficult. They may contain grammatical structures you have not studied, or expressions and sayings you are not familiar with. Unlike graded readers, they have not been written for language students. The words have been chosen to create a particular effect, not because they are easy or difficult. But you do not need to understand every word to understand and enjoy the story.

When you are reading in your own language you will often read so quickly that you skip over words, and read for the general effect, rather than the details. Try to do the same when you are reading in English. Remember that looking up every word you don't know slows you down and stops you enjoying the story.

When you're reading authentic short stories, remember:
– It should be a pleasure!
– You should read at your own pace.
– Let the story carry you along – don't worry about looking up every word you don't understand.
– Don't worry about looking up difficult words unless they stop you from understanding the story.
– Try not to use the *Glossary* or a dictionary when you're reading.

You might want to make a note of words to look up later, especially key words that you see several times (see *Using a dictionary* on page 9 for more tips on looking up and recording new words). But remember, you can always go back again when you have finished the story. That is the beauty of reading short stories – they are short! You can finish one quite quickly, especially if you do not worry about understanding every single word; then you can start again at the beginning and take your time to re-read difficult passages and look up key words.

Preparing yourself for a story

It is always a good idea to prepare yourself, mentally, before starting a story.
– Look at the title. What does it tell you about the story? What do you expect the story to be about?
– If there is a summary, read it. This will help you follow the story.

- Quickly read the first few paragraphs and answer these questions:
  Where is it set?
  When is it set?
  Who is the main character?
- As you read, concentrate on following the gist (the general idea) of the story. You can go back and look at the details later. You can use the questions at the end of the story (see *Understanding the story*) to help you understand what is happening.

Tips for dealing with difficult passages

Some stories include particularly difficult passages. They are usually descriptive and give background information, or set the scene. They are generally difficult to follow because they are full of detail. Try to read these passages quickly, understanding what you can, and then continue with the story. Make a note of the passage and come back to it later, when you have finished the whole story.

If, at any time, you are finding it difficult to follow the story, go back to this difficult passage. It may hold the answers to your questions.

Read through the passage again carefully and underline all the unknown words. Try to understand as much as you can from the immediate context and what you now know about the story. Then, look up any remaining words in the *Glossary* at the back of the book, or in your dictionary.

Tips for dealing with difficult words

- Decide if the word (or phrase) is important to the overall message. Read the whole paragraph. Do you understand the general meaning? Yes? Then the word isn't important. Don't worry about it. *Keep reading!*
- If you decide the word is important, see if you can work out its meaning from the context. Is it a verb, a noun or an adjective? Is it positive or negative? How would you translate it into in your own language? Underline the word or make a note of it and the page number, but *keep reading*. If it really is important, you'll see it again.
- If you keep seeing the same word in the story, and you still can't understand it, look in your monolingual dictionary!

Using a dictionary

Looking up words

Before you look up the word, look at it again in its context. Decide what part of speech it is. Try to guess its meaning from the context. Now look it up in your dictionary. There may be more than one definition given. Decide which one is the most appropriate. If the word is something very specific, eg the name of a flower or tree, you can use a bilingual dictionary to give you the exact translation.

Let's look at how this works in practice. Look at this short extract and follow the instructions below.

> ...there is a little valley or rather **lap** of land among high hills, which is one of the quietest places in the whole world. A small **brook** glides through it, with just murmur enough to **lull** one to repose*
>
> *literary: sleep or rest*
> The Legend of Sleepy Hollow by Washington Irvine

1 Look at the words in bold and decide what part of speech they are – noun, verb, adjective, etc.
2 Try to guess what they might mean.
3 Look at the extracts below from the *Macmillan English Dictionary for Advanced Learners*. Choose the most appropriate definition.

Words with more than one entry
Sometimes the same word belongs to more than one word class: for example, *brook* can be both a noun and a verb. Each word class is shown as a separate entry. The small number at the end of the head-word tells you that a word has more than one entry.

Idioms and fixed expressions
Some words are often used in idioms and fixed expressions. These are shown at the end of the entry, following the small box that says PHRASE.

Words with more than one meaning
Many words have more than one meaning, and each different meaning is shown by a number.

brook¹ noun
a small river
brook² verb
not brook – to definitely not allow or accept something.
lap¹ noun
1 the top half of your legs above your knees when you sit down.
2 one complete turn around a course in a race
PHRASE in the lap of luxury in very comfortable and expensive conditions
lap² verb
1 if an animal laps water, it drinks it gently with its tongue
lull¹ noun
a quiet period during a very active or violent situation
lull² verb
1 to make someone feel relaxed and confident so that they are not prepared for something unpleasant to happen to lull someone into a false sense of security
2 to make someone relaxed enough to go to sleep

Dictionary extracts adapted from the Macmillan English Dictionary © Macmillan Publishers Limited 2002.

Keeping a record

When you have looked in your dictionary, decide if the word is interesting or useful to you. If it is, make a note of it, and write down its definition. Make a note of the sentence where you found it in the story, then write one or two more examples of your own. Only do this for those words you think you will need to use in the future.

Here is an example of how you might record the word *lull*.

'with just murmur enough to lull one to repose'
Lull – to make you feel relaxed enough to go to sleep
e.g. The quiet sound of the waves lulled me to sleep
The mother sang to her baby to lull it to sleep

Literary analysis

The *Literary analysis* section is written to encourage you to consider the stories in more depth. This will help you to appreciate them better and develop your analytical skills. This section is particularly useful for those students who are studying, or intending to study, literature in the medium of English. Each section includes literary terms with which you may or may not be familiar.

Macmillan Readers student's site

For more help with understanding these literary terms, and to find Answer keys to all the exercises and activities, visit the student's section of the Macmillan Readers' website at www.macmillanenglish.com/readers. There you will also find a wealth of resources to help your language learning in English; from listening exercises to articles on acedemic and creative writing.

The genre of Love

What is Love?

Love stories belong to the genre usually described as *Romance*. The Romance sections of bookshops and libraries are popular with many readers, especially women.

Traditionally, love stories are about the romantic relationships of men and women. Popular romantic fiction follows a certain pattern. The main characters meet and are attracted to each other. However, events that they cannot control put obstacles in the way of their love. The hero and heroine must overcome these problems in order to find their 'happy ending,' so that they can be together and possibly marry.

Why do we like love stories?

People like romance stories because they focus on love, a universal emotion, and they are interested in the problems connected to it. Most people have experienced being in love or feeling love for someone. The more popular romantic fiction also allows the reader to escape from the real world – there may be difficulties, but love will win in the end.

Of course, not all love stories end happily and some are very sad. The more literary school of romantic fiction tends not to follow the above model. Instead, these more literary works tend to look at love from many angles.

Romance fiction in English

Love has always been of interest to writers. Geoffrey Chaucer (1340–1400) wrote about love in poems such as *The Canterbury Tales* and *Troilus and Cressida*. Chaucer and other poets of his age were influenced by the poet-musicians of 12th-century France who often sang about 'courtly' love. Courtly love described a kind of behaviour which idealised the love of a knight[1] for a noblewoman (a woman of high birth), who was often married. The long English poem *Sir Gawain and the Green Knight* (c. 1375), by an anonymous writer, is probably the most famous example of this idea. Even today, we sometimes refer to men as 'knights in shining armour,' that is, men who rescue women from difficult situations.

1 in the past, a European soldier who rode a horse

The poets of the 16th and 17th centuries began to move away from the courtly love tradition. They described a wider range of feelings and a more realistic type of love. The metaphysical poets, John Donne, George Herbert and Andrew Marvell, all wrote about the dificulties of love, and treated their lovers more as equals.

> **knight** in the past, a European soldier from a high social class who wore a suit of armour (a metal suit) and rode a horse

This new realism was adopted by the dramatists. The most important of these was Shakespeare. His most famous love story is the play *Romeo and Juliet* (1597), about two young people from families that hate each other. This hatred eventually causes the death of the young lovers. Several films have been made based on the story, including *West Side Story*.

Some of the best early writers of romantic fiction were Jane Austen (1775–1817) and the Bronté sisters, Emily (1818–1848), and Charlotte (1816–1855). Austen's novels, such as *Pride and Prejudice* and *Sense and Sensibility*, are mainly about women's search for suitable husbands. Emily Bronte's *Wuthering Heights* (1847) is about obsessive love and doomed[2] passion. Her sister Charlotte's novel, *Jane Eyre* (1847), tells the story of a young governess's[3] love for her rich, older employer.

> **doomed** sure to fail or suffer something unpleasant
> **governess** in the past, a woman whose job was to teach children in their own homes

Short stories and romance

Romance fits well into the short-story format. The emotions involved create conflict which can be resolved in a number of different ways.

Newspapers and magazines often published short stories with romantic themes. The rise of women's magazines in particular caused a rise in the demand for short pieces of complete fiction. This continues today. Many short stories are written from the woman's point of view.

Some writers wrote short stories to make money while they worked on their latest novel. This was the case for H.G. Wells and H.E. Bates. The quality of their stories is probably inferior to that of their novels. However, that is not always the case. D.H. Lawrence is best known for

2 certain to fail
3 a woman whose job was to teach her employer's children in their home

his novels but wrote some very impressive short stories. We can say the same of F. Scott Fitzgerald or Ernest Hemingway. Some writers made the short story into an art form and wrote little else: this was the case for, for example, Katherine Mansfield, who wrote mainly about love and relationships.

Other forms

Stories with romantic themes are often made into films for the cinema and TV, and short stories particularly, are often adapted for TV or radio.

Jane Austen's novels have been made into films and also serialised for TV. One of her most famous characters, Mr Darcy, in *Pride and Prejudice*, appears as a fantasy figure in the contemporary novel *Bridget Jones's Diary* (1996) by Helen Fielding. In the film based on Fielding's book, the man who Bridget eventually falls in love with is played by the actor Colin Firth, who also plays Darcy in the TV version of *Pride and Prejudice*.

Other famous films based on love stories include *Gone with the Wind* by Margaret Mitchell, *A Farewell to Arms* by Ernest Hemingway, *The Great Gatsby* by F. Scott Fitzgerald, *Women in Love* by D.H.Lawrence, *The End of the Affair* by Graham Greene and *The English Patient* by Michael Ondaatje.

A recent development in romantic fiction is the emergence of 'chick lit', that is, literature intended especially for women, which is often about a romantic relationship. The women in the stories are often in their twenties or thirties and work in cities. The stories follow their love lives and struggles for professional success.

These days, it is possible to write one's own love story and publish it on the Internet. Some personal websites contain 'blogs', or diaries which describe the writer's romantic adventures. Some blogs have even been published in book form.

Second Best

by D H Lawrence

About the author

David Herbert Lawrence was the youngest son of five children, known as 'Bert' to his family. He was born in 1885 in the mining village of Eastwood, near the city of Nottingham in central England. His father was a miner and his mother had been a school teacher before she married. The difference in their backgrounds and education caused a lot of problems in their marriage. Mrs Lawrence was disappointed with her life. She wanted her children's lives to be better – she did not want her daughters to become servants or her sons to become miners. She was therefore very proud when her youngest son, David, won a scholarship[1] to Nottingham High School. Unfortunately, Lawrence did not do well at school, and when he left in 1901, he worked for a short time as a factory clerk. After a long illness, he became a student and teacher at the British School in Eastwood, where he stayed for three years. This time he was more successful, and in 1904, Lawrence achieved a First[2] class degree in the King's Scholarship exam and went on to study for his teacher's certificate at University College Nottingham.

In 1908, Lawrence moved to London where he continued to teach, and write. In 1909, his first poems were published, thanks to his first girlfriend, Jessie Chambers. Jesse sent them to a magazine, the *English Review*. It continued to publish his work throughout his life.

In March 1912, Lawrence fell in love with Frieda von Richthofen, a minor German aristocrat. Frieda was six years older than Lawrence. She was already married, to his former professor at Nottingham University; she had three young children. Despite this, Frieda ran away with Lawrence to the German town of Metz, her home town. Their timing was bad – in the years leading up to the First World War, there was very little trust between the Germans and the British. Lawrence was

1 an amount of money that an organisation gives to someone so that they can study at a particular school or university
2 in the UK and Australia, the highest mark for an undergraduate degree at a university

accused of being a spy[3], although he was eventually released. Lawrence and Frieda lived for a short time in Italy, and then returned to England. They finally married in 1914, after Frieda got her divorce. Life in England was difficult for the Lawrences. Many people disapproved of their marriage, and there was a lot of anti-German feeling because of the War. Lawrence continued to write, and to publish, but many people were hostile towards his work – his honest descriptions of love and relationships were considered shocking at the time. Indeed, two of his most famous novels, *Lady Chatterley's Lover* and *The Rainbow*, were banned. Lawrence longed to escape to the USA, but he could not get a visa for himself and Frieda.

In 1915, the couple moved to Cornwall where Lawrence finally finished his novel *Women in Love*, which he had begun writing as a teenager. The couple's lives remained difficult – Lawrence was ill, they had little money, but he continued to earn a living from his writing.

However, people continued to be suspicious about the couple's connections with Germany and in 1919, after the war, the Lawrences left England for Europe. They lived in Italy, Malta, Austria and Germany. Lawrence continued to write novels, poetry and some non-fiction. He wrote a history book which was used in English schools. However, it was published under a pseudonym[4] because of Lawrence's bad reputation. Lawrence returned twice to England for short visits, but he continued to write about Eastwood and called it 'the country of my heart'.

In 1922, the Lawrences left Europe and travelled more widely. But ultimately, poor health brought them back to Italy, and they bought a villa near Florence. Here, Lawrence wrote his last major novel, *Lady Chatterley's Lover*, about an aristocratic woman who falls in love with a gamekeeper[5]. His health worsened and on 2nd March 1930, Lawrence died from tuberculosis in Vence, France. He was 44 years old.

Lawrence was an unconventional[6] man both in his lifestyle and his writings. On the whole, his work was not understood or fully appreciated in his lifetime. After his death, Lawrence's reputation continued to grow. Several of his novels became very well known, particularly *Sons and Lovers*, *Women in Love*, *The Rainbow* and *Lady Chatterley's Lover*.

3   someone whose job it is to find out secret information about an organisation or
    country
4   a name that someone uses that is not their real name, especially for writing a book
5   someone whose job is to look after the wild animals on a piece of private land and to
    stop anyone from hunting them without permission
6   different from what people consider to be usual or normal

Lawrence's background and experiences growing up in a mining village, led to his belief that increasing industrialisation degraded people and caused workers to live a life of ugliness. He believed that people needed beauty to live, and he was extremely sensitive to all forms of beauty in nature. His best work reveals his love of life and living things, and his understanding of the relations between men and women.

About the story

The story *Second Best* was written in the summer of 1911 and was published in the *English Review* in 1912. In 1914, it was included in the collection *The Prussian Officer and Other Stories*.

Background information

Speech patterns and social class

The story is set in the British countryside, in an area called the Midlands, and small villages can be seen in the distance. This landscape, a mixture of agricultural land and encroaching[7] industry, is probably similar to the area around Eastwood, where Lawrence grew up.

The younger sister in the story, Anne, still lives at home and speaks with a Midlands dialect and accent. The main male character in the story, Tom Smedley, works on the land and speaks in a similar way. Frances, Anne's older sister – who works away from home in the city of Liverpool – does not use a Midlands dialect and generally thinks that it is vulgar[8]. At the same time, she does not seem to judge people by the way they speak – Lawrence tells us she doesn't mind the way that Tom speaks. But the man she really cares about is Jimmy, an educated man and a gentleman. However, she also thinks that Jimmy is *something of a snob*[9] which may reflect the way that someone of Frances's social class would see someone who has left their roots behind and 'gone up' in the world.

Despite her own background, Anne is aware of the way people speak, and she doesn't like it when Tom's accent and dialect become

7 gradually covering more land; taking power or authority
8 *old-fashioned:* rude, unpleasant, offensive
9 *British:* someone who thinks and behaves as if they are better than other people, usually because of their social class; someone who thinks their opinions and judgments are better than other people's

stronger. She says to him, *I can't bear you to talk broad* (with a strong accent). Lawrence's mother and father probably talked in ways that showed the difference in their social backgrounds. His father was a miner and no doubt had a broader accent and used more dialect than his wife, who was more educated. This may have caused tension when Lawrence was a boy. We can imagine his mother telling the children to 'speak properly'. (In the story, Frances says to Tom: *I like you to talk NICELY.* Anne is also annoyed that Tom took a servant girl to the Ollerton Feast. We know that Lawrence's mother did not want her daughters to be servants. Anne and Frances believed themselves to be 'higher up the social ladder' than a servant.

Summary

It may help you to know something about what happens in the story before you read it. Don't worry, this summary does not tell you how the story ends!

The story is written in the third person. Frances, who normally works in the city of Liverpool, is visiting her family village. It is the day after her arrival and she is in the countryside with her fourteen-year-old sister Anne. It is a hot day and Frances is tired. Anne tells her sister about Tom Smedley, who has given her a wild rabbit. Anne says that Tom promised to take her to Ollerton Feast but took another girl instead, a servant. Anne told Tom he had no right to do this and that she would tell her sister. Frances says that Tom can take whomever he wants, but she laughs when Anne insists it wasn't right because he had promised to take her.

Anne sees a rabbit hole and the two sisters sit still and wait for the rabbit to appear. Frances finds the surroundings oppressive[10], which reflects her own tiredness. Suddenly a mole appears, moving slowly over the ground. These little creatures are pests[11] and, normally, Frances would tell Anne to kill it immediately. Today, however, she feels too unhappy and lethargic[12] to suggest it. She notices that the animal seems to be enjoying the sunshine and feels *a keen pity* for the animal. Anne sees the mole and puts her foot on it. Frances tells

10 hot in an unpleasant way, especially if there is no wind; something that is oppressive makes you very worried or unhappy
11 insects or small animals that damage plants or supplies of food
12 lacking energy and not wanting to do anything

her sister to kill it and turns her face away. Anne puts the mole in a handkerchief with the intention of taking it home for her father or someone else to kill.

Anne asks Frances if she has seen Jimmy Barrass recently. Frances tells her that Jimmy is engaged to be married. It is clear that Frances is upset about this.

The mole escapes from the handkerchief and bites Anne. Angrily, she takes her sister's walking cane and kills the animal. Though she feels shock at first, Frances no longer feels pity for the creature. She doesn't seem to care about anyone or anything.

The two girls walk through the fields and meet Tom, a young man who has known Frances for years. He is attracted to her but she has never given him any encouragement. She has had strong feelings for Jimmy for five years, but Jimmy felt only *half-measures* for her.

Frances knows Tom likes her; she decides that if she cannot have Jimmy, she will have Tom, though he is only *second best*.

Pre-reading exercises

Key vocabulary

This section will help you familiarise yourself with some of the more specific vocabulary used in the story. You may want to use it to help you before you start reading, or as a revision exercise after you have finished reading.

Verbs describing movement

Lawrence was a very keen observer of nature and animals. His descriptions of the mole and its movements are particularly detailed.

1 **Look at the verbs and definitions in the box below; match the verbs with the correct definition.**

1 **nose**	a) to walk slowly and carefully without lifting your feet
2 **snuff**	b) to swim slowly by moving your arms and legs gently through the water
3 **shuffle**	c) to move forward slowly and carefully
4 **paddle**	d) to breathe in noisily through your nose

2 Which verbs suggest that the mole is finding its way by using its sense of smell?

Lawrence uses the verbs below to describe the mole's movements as it tries to escape from under Anne's foot and then from her handkerchief.

struggle	to try hard to do something that you find difficult
twist	to bend or turn in a different direction
twitch	to make a sudden quick movement
wrestle	to fight by trying to throw your opponent to the ground
wriggle	to move by twisting and turning quickly
heave	to move up and down with a large, regular movement
row	to move a boat through water using long flat poles (oars)
writhe	to move by twisting and turning, especially when you feel a lot of pain

3 Which two verbs (one from each list above) are connected with water? Are these verbs appropriate to describe the mole? What do they suggest about the mole's movements?

4 Complete these sentences with one of the verbs from the boxes above.

1 The old woman .... slowly towards the door.
2 Little by little, the lorry .... its way through the heavy traffic.
3 The boy .... to understand the difficult maths problem.
4 When I am nervous, my left eye always ....
5 After he fell off the horse, the man was .... in pain.
6 This child never keeps still; he's always ....

The use of adverbs

Look at the beginning of the story.

'Oh, I'm tired!' Frances exclaimed **petulantly**.

The adverb tells us something about how Frances is feeling. She is tired but she is also *petulant* or feeling sorry for herself.

Lawrence often uses adverbs to describe mood and character.

5 **Make adverbs from the adjectives below. Then write a suitable adverb in the gap in the sentences that follow. We have done the first one for you, as an example.**

significant   cold   ~~petulant~~   tentative   decisive   faltering
sarcastic   breathless   indifferent   defiant

1 'Oh, I'm tired!' Frances exclaimed ..._petulantly_.... .
2 'Right! I've made my mind up,' said the manager .... at the end of the interview. 'Mrs Jones definitely gets the job.'
3 'I don't care which restaurant we go to', said Meg .... 'They're all the same to me.'
4 Sarah was wearing high heels for the first time. Blushing a little, she walked .... into the party.
5 'I won't do it, so there!' the child shouted .... at the teacher.
6 'Will you ... I mean, would you, perhaps ... go out with me?' he asked ....
7 'What's that?' shrieked Fran when she saw the dog.
'What do you think it is? A canary?' retorted her brother, ...
8 'So, you don't love me, then,' he said.
'No, I don't,' she said .... , her face like a mask. 'It was all in your imagination.'
9 'What did you buy Tim for his birthday?' asked Mrs Duncan.
'Er, I'll tell you LATER... .' said her husband .... , as little Tim walked into the room.
10 When the phone rang, Sue ran across to it in great excitement. 'Oh, who can it be?' she asked ....

Describing the countryside

6 **Look at this description of the countryside on a hot day. Complete the description with the phrases in the box below.**

not clear   touched by fire   about to burst into flame
without life   strong light   white   shone

The fields were (1 ....), bleached by the strong sunlight.
The sun (2 ....) down on the oak trees. Their leaves

*looked brown and scorched, as if (3 ....). The day was
(4 ....); there was a haze over everything. The flowers
looked limp, (5 ....). The girls covered their eyes from the
(6 ....), the blinding glare of the sun. Everything seemed to
be in a state of combustion, (7 ....).*

When you have finished the story, look back at this page and check
your answers.

Main themes

Before you read the story, you may want to think about some of its
main themes. The questions will help you think about the story as
you're reading it for the first time. There is more discussion of the main
themes in the *Literary analysis* section after the story.

Relationships between men and women

In many of his stories, Lawrence explores the relationships between
men and women. There is often tension behind the words of his male
and female characters and a lot of the real communication is made
without words. His characters feel deeply and suffer for love. This is
true in *Second Best*. Lawrence writes: *Anne was in her unvexed teens;
men were like big dogs to her: while Frances, at twenty-three, suffered a
good deal.* Tom also, at the end of the story *stood, suffering, resisting his
passion for her.*

There is tension in the conversation between Frances and Tom and
their words are a way of flirting[13] and trying to discover each other's
intentions. Anne is not really aware of this – *I don't know what you
two's been jawing about, I'm sure*, she says after they leave Tom.

? As you read the story, ask yourself:

a) How does Lawrence portray[14] the changing emotions of his
   characters?
b) Do people really experience feelings in this way?

13 behaving towards someone in a way which shows your sexual or romantic interest in
   them
14 *formal, literary:* show or describe someone in a particular way

The mystery of nature

Another of Lawrence's main themes is the beauty and power of nature. But he is not sentimental[15] about nature and he knows it can be cruel too. His landscapes reflect reality: in *Second Best*, the weather is hot and the landscape – like the people – suffers because of it. On page 24, for example, *the hillside gave off heat in silence; the brown earth seemed in a low state of combustion, the leaves of the oak were scorched brown.* On page 26, Frances looks at *the exhausted, limp leaves of the primroses.*

The mole is described as a *little brute*, its movements are *pitiful* or *frantic*, it is *clumsy*, a *vicious little nuisance.* But after she has killed it, Anne is filled with wonder at its beautiful skin. Frances, because she is feeling very sensitive herself, at first feels sorry for the animal, then is shocked at its death and finally reaches a state of acceptance: *I suppose they have to be killed.* Anne and Frances are country girls – they must not be sentimental about an animal that damages the land.

Above all, Lawrence is interested in the 'life force' or spirit that unites people, animals and all of nature. So, often, his descriptions of landscapes tell us something about the characters or love. For example, there is a similarity between the blindness of the mole and the unconscious nature of Tom's passion for Frances.

8 As you read the story, ask yourself:

a) Does the landscape in the story have its own character, or is it just a reflection of people's feelings?

b) How does Lawrence feel about the mole? Is killing it, and the way it is killed, important in the story? Why?

---

15 relating to emotions rather than reason

Second Best

by D H Lawrence

'Oh, I'm tired!' Frances exclaimed petulantly, and in the same instant she dropped down on the turf[16], near the hedge-bottom[17]. Anne stood a moment surprised, then, accustomed to the vagaries[18] of her beloved[19] Frances, said:

'Well, and aren't you always likely to be tired, after travelling that blessed[20] long way from Liverpool yesterday?' and she plumped down beside her sister. Anne was a wise young body[21] of fourteen, very buxom, brimming with common sense. Frances was much older, about twenty-three, and **whimsical**, **spasmodic**. She was the beauty and the clever child of the family. She plucked the goose-grass[22] buttons from her dress in nervous, desperate fashion. Her beautiful profile, looped[23] above with black hair, warm with the dusky-and-scarlet **complexion** of a pear, was calm as a mask, her thin brown hand plucked nervously.

'It's not the journey,' she said, objecting to Anne's **obtuseness**. Anne looked inquiringly at her darling. The young girl, in her self-confident, practical way, proceeded to reckon up[24] this whimsical creature. But suddenly she found herself full in the eyes of Frances; felt two dark, hectic eyes flaring challenge at her, and she shrank away. Frances was **peculiar** for these great, exposed looks, which disconcerted people by their violence and their suddenness.

---

16 short grass and the earth that is under it
17 the bottom of a line of small trees or bushes
18 *old-fashioned*: unexpected changes that you cannot control
19 *formal, literary*: someone or something that you love very much
20 *colloquial, old-fashioned*: used for emphasizing that you are annoyed about something; the second 'e' is pronounced
21 *literary*: person
22 clumps of fluff or fabric on her dress
23 loop *(noun)* a round shape or curve made by a line curving back towards itself
24 *old-fashioned, literary*: contemplate, look at

'What's a matter, poor old duck[25]?' asked Anne, as she folded the slight, wilful form of her sister in her arms. Frances laughed shakily, and nestled down for comfort on the budding breasts of the strong girl.

'Oh, I'm only a bit tired,' she murmured, on the point of tears.

'Well, of course you are, what do you expect?' soothed Anne. It was a joke to Frances that Anne should play elder, almost mother to her. But then, Anne was in her unvexed[26] **teens**; men were like big dogs to her: while Frances, at twenty-three, suffered a good deal.

The country was intensely morning-still. On the common[27] everything shone beside its shadow, and the hillside gave off heat in silence. The brown turf seemed in a low state of combustion[28], the leaves of the oaks were scorched brown. Among the blackish foliage[29] in the distance shone the small red and orange of the village.

The willows in the brook-course[30] at the foot of the common[31] suddenly shook with a dazzling effect like diamonds. It was a puff of wind. Anne resumed her normal position. She spread her knees, and put in her lap a handful of hazel nuts, whity-green leafy things, whose one cheek was tanned between brown and pink. These she began to crack and eat. Frances, with bowed head, **mused** bitterly.

'Eh, you know Tom Smedley?' began the young girl, as she pulled a tight kernel out of its shell.

'I suppose so,' replied Frances sarcastically.

'Well, he gave me a wild rabbit what he'd caught, to keep with my tame one – and it's living.'

25 *dialect*: dear
26 *unusual*: not worried
27 a large piece of open land near a village or town where anyone can walk, play sports etc.
28 the process of burning
29 the leaves of a plant or tree
30 the path of a small stream
31 a large piece of open land in a village or town where anyone can walk, play sports etc

'That's a good thing,' said Frances, very detached and ironic.

'Well, it *is*! He reckoned he'd take me to Ollerton Feast, but he never did. Look here, he took a servant from the rectory[32]; I saw him.'

'So he ought,' said Frances.

'No, he oughtn't! and I told him so. And I told him I should tell you – an' I have done.'

Click and snap went a nut between her teeth. She sorted out the kernel, and chewed complacently.

'It doesn't make much difference,' said Frances.

'Well, 'appen it doesn't; but I was mad with him all the same.'

'Why?'

'Because I was; he's no right to go with a servant.'

'He's a perfect right,' persisted Frances, very just and cold.

'No, he hasn't, when he'd said he'd take me.'

Frances burst into a laugh of amusement and relief.

'Oh, no; I'd forgot that,' she said, adding, 'And what did he say when you promised to tell me?'

'He laughed and said, 'She won't fret her fat[33] over that.''

'And she won't,' sniffed Frances.

There was silence. The common, with its sere[34], blonde-headed thistles, its heaps of silent bramble, its brown-**husked** gorse[35] in the **flare** of sunshine, seemed visionary[36]. Across the brook began the immense pattern of agriculture, white chequering[37] of barley stubble, brown squares of wheat, khaki patches of pasture, red stripes of fallow[38], with the woodland and the tiny village dark like ornaments, leading away to the distance, right to the hills, where the check-pattern grew smaller and smaller, till, in the blackish haze of heat, far off, only the tiny white squares of barley stubble showed distinct.

32 a house where the rector, or priest, of a church lives

33 *dialect, phrase, 'fret her fat'*: worry or care

34 dried up

35 a low bush with yellow flowers and thorns

36 here, 'like a vision'

37 *literary:* with a pattern or design of squares

38 *usually an adjective*: land that has been ploughed but does not have crops growing on it

'Eh, I say, here's a rabbit hole!' cried Anne suddenly. 'Should we watch if one comes out? You won't have to **fidget**, you know.'

The two girls sat perfectly still. Frances watched certain objects in her surroundings: they had a peculiar, unfriendly look about them: the weight of greenish elderberries on their purpling[39] stalks; the twinkling of the yellowing crab-apples that **clustered** high up in the hedge, against the sky: the exhausted, limp leaves of the primroses lying flat in the hedge-bottom: all looked strange to her. Then her eyes caught a movement. A **mole** was moving silently over the warm, red soil, nosing, **shuffling** hither and thither[40], flat, and dark as a shadow, shifting about, and as suddenly brisk, and as silent, like a very ghost of joie de vivre[41]. Frances started[42], from habit was about to call on Anne to kill the little pest. But, to-day, her lethargy of unhappiness was too much for her. She watched the little brute[43] **paddling**, snuffing, touching things to discover them, running in blindness, delighted to ecstasy by the sunlight and the hot, strange things that caressed its belly and its nose. She felt a keen pity for the little creature.

'Eh, our Fran, look there! It's a mole.'

Anne was on her feet, standing watching the dark unconscious beast[44]. Frances frowned with anxiety.

'It doesn't run off, does it?' said the young girl softly. Then she **stealthily** approached the creature. The mole paddled fumblingly[45] away. In an instant Anne put her foot upon it, not too heavily. Frances could see the **struggling**, swimming movement of the little pink hands of the brute, the twisting and twitching of its pointed nose, as it **wrestled** under the sole of the boot.

39 *literary:* turning or becoming purple
40 *old-fashioned, literary (adverbial phrase):* in many different directions
41 *French phrase (used in English), 'joy of living':* a feeling of pleasure or excitement that comes from enjoying life
42 *old-fashioned:* jump with fright
43 a strong animal who acts in a cruel or violent way (unusual to describe a small creature)
44 *mainly literary:* animal, especially a dangerous or strange one
45 *usually used as verb, 'fumble':* to try to hold, move, or find something using your hands in a way that is not skilful or graceful

'It *does* **wriggle**!' said the bonny girl, **knitting her brows** in a frown at the eerie sensation. Then she bent down to look at her trap. Frances could now see, beyond the edge of the boot-sole, frantic **rowing** of the flat pink hands.

'Kill the thing,' she said, turning away her face.

'Oh – I'm not,' laughed Anne, shrinking. 'You can, if you like.'

'I *don't* like,' said Frances, with quiet intensity.

After several dabbing attempts, Anne succeeded in picking up the little animal by the **scruff** of its neck. It threw back its head, flung its long blind **snout** from side to side, the mouth open in a peculiar oblong[46], with tiny pinkish teeth at the edge. The blind, frantic mouth gaped and **writhed**. The body, heavy and clumsy, hung scarcely moving.

'Isn't it a **snappy** little thing,' observed Anne, twisting to avoid the teeth.

'What are you going to do with it?' asked Frances sharply.

'It's got to be killed – look at the damage they do. I s'll take it home and let dada[47] or somebody kill it. I'm not going to let it go.'

She swaddled[48] the creature clumsily in her pocket-handkerchief and sat down beside her sister. There as an interval of silence, during which Anne combated[49] the efforts of the mole.

'You've not had much to say about Jimmy this time. Did you see him often in Liverpool?' Anne asked suddenly.

'Once or twice,' replied Frances, giving no sign of how the question troubled her.

'And aren't you sweet on[50] him any more, then?'

'I should think I'm not, seeing that he's engaged.'

'Engaged? Jimmy Barrass! Well, of all things! I never thought *he'd* get engaged.'

46 rectangle
47 *dialect:* father, daddy
48 usually used to describe wrapping a baby very tightly in a blanket
49 fought
50 *colloquial, old-fashioned:* to be attracted to someone in a romantic way

'Why not, he's as much right as anybody else?' snapped Frances.

Anne was fumbling with the mole. "Appen so[51]," she said at length; 'but I never thought Jimmy would, though.'

'Why not?' snapped Frances.

'I don't know – this blessed mole, it'll not keep still! – who's he got engaged to?'

'How should I know?'

'I thought you'd ask him; you've known him long enough. I s'd think he thought he'd get engaged now he's a Doctor of Chemistry.'

Frances laughed in spite of herself.

'What's that got to do with it?' she asked.

'I'm sure it's got a lot. He'll want to feel *somebody* now, so he's got engaged. Hey, stop it; go in!'

But at this juncture[52] the mole almost succeeded in wriggling clear. It wrestled and twisted frantically, waved its pointed blind head, its mouth standing open like a little shaft, its big, wrinkled hands spread out.

'Go in with you!' urged Anne, poking the little creature with her forefinger, trying to get it back into the handkerchief. Suddenly the mouth turned like a spark on her finger.

'Oh!' she cried, 'he's bit me.'

She dropped him to the floor. Dazed, the blind creature fumbled round. Frances felt like shrieking. She expected him to dart[53] away in a flash, like a mouse, and there he remained **groping**; she wanted to cry to him to be gone. Anne, in a sudden decision of wrath[54], caught up her sister's walking-cane. With one blow[55] the mole was dead. Frances was startled and shocked. One moment the little **wretch** was fussing in the heat, and the next it lay like a little bag, inert[56] and black – not a struggle, scarce[57] a **quiver**.

51 *dialect, colloquial:* 'I suppose so'; 'I accept that'
52 *formal, phrase: 'at this juncture':* at this stage in the process; now
53 to make a sudden quick movement
54 *formal:* very great anger
55 a hard hit from someone's hand or object
56 *technical:* not moving
57 *old-fashioned, literary:* almost not, almost none

'It is dead!' Frances said breathlessly. Anne took her finger from her mouth, looked at the tiny pinpricks[58], and said:

'Yes, he is, and I'm glad. They're **vicious** little nuisances, moles are.'

With which her wrath vanished. She picked up the dead animal.

'Hasn't it got a beautiful skin,' she mused, stroking the fur with a forefinger, then with her cheek.

'Mind[59],' said Frances sharply. 'You'll have the blood on your skirt!'

One ruby drop of blood hung on the small snout, ready to fall. Anne shook it off on to some harebells[60]. Frances suddenly became calm; in that moment, grown-up.

'I suppose they have to be killed,' she said, and a certain rather dreary indifference succeeded[61] to her grief. The twinkling crab-apples, the glitter of brilliant willows now seemed to her trifling, scarcely worth the notice. Something had died in her, so that things lost their poignancy. She was calm, indifference overlying her quiet sadness. Rising, she walked down to the brook course.

'Here, wait for me,' cried Anne, coming tumbling after.

Frances stood on the bridge, looking at the red mud trodden into pockets by the feet of cattle. There was not a **drain** of water left, but everything smelled green, succulent. Whey did she care so little for Anne, who was so fond of her? She asked herself. Why did she care so little for anyone? She did not know, but she felt a rather stubborn pride in her isolation and indifference.

They entered a field where stooks[62] of barley stood in rows, the straight, blonde tresses[63] of the corn streaming on to the ground. The stubble was bleached by the intense summer, so that the expanse glared white. The next field was sweet and soft with a second crop of seeds; thin, straggling clover whose little

---

58 a very small round spot of something, as though caused by a pin
59 *dialect:* be careful
60 a wild plant with small pale blue flowers shaped like bells
61 to follow or replace someone or something
62 a heap or bundle of sheaves of grain
63 long pieces, usually of a woman's hair

pink knobs rested prettily in the dark green. The scent was faint and **sickly**. The girls came up **in single file**, Frances leading.

Near the gate a young man was **mowing** with the scythe[64] some fodder[65] for the afternoon feed of the cattle. As he saw the girls he left off[66] working and waited in an aimless kind of way. Frances was dressed in white muslin[67], and she walked with dignity, detailed and forgetful. Her lack of agitation, her simple, unheeding[68] advance made him nervous. She had loved the far-off[69] Jimmy for five years, having had in return his half-measures[70]. This man only affected her slightly.

Tom was of medium stature[71], energetic in build[72]. His smooth, fair-skinned face was burned red, not brown, by the sun, and this ruddiness[73] enhanced his appearance of good humour and easiness. Being a year older than Frances, he would have courted[74] her long ago had she been so inclined. As it was, he had gone his uneventful way amiably, chatting with many a girl, but remaining unattached, free of trouble for the most part. Only he knew he wanted a woman. He **hitched** his trousers just a trifle[75] self-consciously as the girls approached. Frances was a rare, delicate kind of being, whom he realized with a queer and delicious stimulation in his veins. She gave him a slight sense of **suffocation**. Somehow, this morning, she affected him more than usual. She was dressed in white. He, however, being **matter-of-fact** in his mind, did not realize. His feeling had never become conscious, purposive[76].

64　a tool used for cutting long grass or grain
65　food, especially hay or straw, to feed animals such as cows and horses
66　stopped doing something
67　a light thin cotton cloth
68　*mainly literary:* paying no attention, without thought
69　distant
70　action that fails to deal with something completely or effectively; here, 'half-hearted actions/feelings'
71　*mainly literary:* height
72　*formal:* size and shape of a body
73　red and healthy look
74　*old-fashioned:* to (pursue, or try to) have a romantic relationship with someone, usually leading to marriage
75　*old fashioned:* something that is not very important, a small amount
76　*old-fashioned, literary, very unusual:* with an aim or purpose

Frances knew what she was about. Tom was ready to love her as soon as she would show him. Now that she could not have Jimmy, she did not poignantly care. Still, she would have something. If she could not have the best – Jimmy, whom she knew to be something of snob – she would have the second best, Tom. She advanced rather indifferently.

'You are back, then!' said Tom. She marked[77] the touch of uncertainty in his voice.

'No,' she laughed, 'I'm still in Liverpool,' and the undertone of intimacy made him burn.

'This isn't you, then?' he asked.

Her heart leapt up in approval. She looked in his eyes, and for a second was with him.

'Why, what do you think?' she laughed.

He lifted his hat from his head with a distracted little gesture. She liked him, his quaint ways, his humour, his ignorance, and his slow masculinity.

'Here, look here, Tom Smedley,' broke in Anne.

'A moudiwarp[78]! Did you find it dead?' he asked.

'No, it bit me,' said Anne.

'Oh, aye[79]! An' that got your rag out[80], did it?'

'No, it didn't!' Anne scolded sharply. 'Such language!'

'Oh, what's up wi' it[81]?'

'I can't bear you to talk broad.'

'Can't you?'

He glanced at Frances.

'It isn't nice,' Frances said. She did not care, really. The vulgar speech **jarred** on her **as a rule**; Jimmy was a gentleman. But Tom's manner of speech did not matter to her.

'I like you to talk *nicely*,' she added.

'Do you,' he replied, **tilting** his hat, stirred.

'And generally you *do*, you know,' she smiled.

'I s'll have to have a try,' he said, rather tensely gallant.

77 *mainly literary:* to notice
78 *dialect:* mole
79 *dialect:* 'yes' or 'really'
80 *dialect, colloquial, phrase: 'to get your rag out':* to annoy you, make you angry
81 *dialect, colloquial, phrase: 'what's up with it':* what's wrong with it, what is the problem

'What?' she asked brightly.

'To talk nice to you,' he said. Frances coloured furiously, bent her head for a moment, then laughed gaily, as if she liked this clumsy hint.

'Eh now, you mind what you're saying,' cried Anne, giving the young man an admonitory pat.

'You wouldn't have to give your mole many knocks like that,' he teased, relieved to get on safe ground, rubbing his arm.

'No indeed, it died in one blow,' said Frances, with a flippancy that was hateful to her.

'You're not so good at knockin' 'em?' he said, turning to her.

'I don't know, if I'm cross,' she said decisively.

'No?' he replied, with alert attentiveness.

'I could,' she added, harder, 'if it was necessary.'

He was slow to feel her difference.

'And don't you consider it *is* necessary?' he asked, with misgiving.

'W-ell-is it?' she said, looking at him steadily, coldly.

'I reckon it is,' he replied, looking away, but standing stubborn.

She laughed quickly.

'But it isn't necessary for *me*,' she said, with slight contempt.

'Yes, that's quite true,' he answered.

She laughed in a shaky fashion.

'*I know it is*,' she said; and there was an awkward pause.

'Why, would you *like* me to kill moles then?' she asked tentatively, after a while.

'They do us a lot of damage,' he said, standing firm on his own ground, angered.

'Well, I'll see the next time I come across one,' she promised, defiantly. Their eyes met, and she sank before him, her pride troubled. He felt uneasy and triumphant and **baffled**, as if fate had gripped him. She smiled as she departed.

'Well,' said Anne, as the sister went through the wheat stubble; 'I don't know what you two's been jawing[82] about, I'm sure.'

82 *dialect, colloquial, unusual:* talking

'Don't you?' laughed Frances significantly.

'No, I don't. But, at any rate, Tom Smedley's a good deal better to my thinking than Jimmy, so there – and nicer.'

'Perhaps he is,' said Frances coldly.

And the next day, after a secret, persistent hunt, she found another mole playing in the heat. She killed it, and in the evening, when Tom came to the gate to smoke his pipe after supper, she took him the dead creature.

'Here you are then!' she said.

'Did you catch it?' he replied, taking the velvet **corpse** into his fingers and examining it minutely. This was to hide his trepidation.

'Did you think I couldn't?' she asked, her face very near his.

'Nay[83], I didn't know.'

She laughed in his face, a strange little laugh that caught her breath, all agitation, and tears, and **recklessness** of desire. He looked frightened and upset. She put her hand to his arm.

'Shall you go out wi' me?' he asked, in a difficult, troubled tone.

She turned her face away, with a shaky laugh. The blood came up in him, strong, overmastering. He resisted it. But it drove him down, and he was carried away. Seeing the winsome[84], frail nape[85]of her neck, fierce love came upon him for her, and tenderness.

'We s'll 'ave to tell your mother,' he said. And he stood, suffering, resisting his passion for her.

'Yes,' she replied, in a dead voice. But there was a thrill of pleasure in this death.

---

83 *dialect, colloquial:* no
84 *mainly literary, old-fashioned:* with an attractive appearance or manner
85 the back of the neck

Post-reading exercises

Understanding the story

1 **Use these questions to help you check that you have understood the story.**

1 Where are Anne and Frances?

2 Why does Anne think that Frances is tired?

3 How does the author describe the sisters' attitude to men?

4 Who begins the conversation about Tom Smedley?

5 What has Tom given to Anne?

6 Why is Anne *mad* (angry) with Tom?

7 Why does Frances laugh with *amusement and relief*?

8 Anne has promised to *tell* her sister about Tom. Does Frances show any interest in Tom's reaction to this?

9 Why do the sisters sit *perfectly still*?

10 How does Frances react when she sees the mole?

11 What do the girls think should be done with the mole?

12 Why does Anne put the mole in her handkerchief?

13 Who begins the conversation about Jimmy?

14 Why is Frances not *sweet on* Jimmy any more?

15 Why does Anne think that Jimmy got engaged?

16 Why does Anne finally kill the mole? How?

17 How does Anne feel after she kills the mole? And Frances?

18 Where do the girls meet Tom? What is he doing?

19 How does Frances feel about Tom?

20 What are Tom's feelings for Frances? How do you know?

21 Do you think Frances intends to flirt with Tom? Why?

22 What is Tom's relationship with Anne?

23 Why does Frances blush when Tom says he will have to try and *talk nice* to her?

24 Why do you think they all spend so much time talking about the mole?

25 What is Anne's final reaction to the conversation?

26 Why does Frances look for a mole the next day and kill it?

27 Why does Tom say *We s'll have to tell your mother*?

28 How would you interpret the last sentence of the story?

Language study

Grammar

Participle clauses with adverbial meaning

Lawrence often uses an *–ing* clause after quoted speech. This is a way of describing what someone is doing, or how they feel, while they are talking.

1 Look at these examples from the story.

> *'Did you catch it?' he replied, **taking** the velvet corpse into his hands and **examining** it minutely.*
>
> *'It's not the journey,' she said, **objecting** to Anne's obtuseness.*
>
> *'It DOES wriggle!' said the bonny girl, **knitting** her brows in a frown at the eerie sensation.*
>
> *'Once or twice,' replied Frances, **giving** no sign of how the question troubled her.*

In which of the sentences in the box above does Lawrence:

a) describe actions
b) describe feelings or attitudes?

2 Rewrite the following sentences as one sentence using an *–ing* clause or clauses. We have done the first one for you, as an example.

1 'Go in with you!' urged Anne. She poked the little creature with her forefinger. She tried to get it back into the handkerchief.
   'Go on with you!' urged Anne, poking the little creature with her forefinger, trying to get it back into the handkerchief.

2 'Hasn't it got a beautiful skin,' she mused. She stroked the fur with her cheek.

3 'Do you,' he replied. He tilted his hat.

4 'You're not so good at knockin' em?' he said. He turned to her.

5 'W-ell-is it?' she said. She looked at him steadily, coldly.

6 'They do us a lot of damage,' he said. He stood firm on his own ground.

Using adverbial phrases to create emphasis – word order

One way of creating emphasis is to put an adverbial phrase at the beginning of a sentence. We can do this to draw attention to the place which is being described. Look at these examples from the story.

> **Across the brook** *began the immense pattern of agriculture…*
> **On the common** *everything shone beside its shadow…*
> **Among the blackish foliage in the distance** *shone the small red and orange of the village.*

3 **Where are the verbs in these sentences? Could they be written in different places?**

4 **Rewrite the following sentences so that the adverbial phrase is placed at the beginning. Write the verb immediately after the adverbial phrase. We have done the first one for you, as an example.**

1 A bright sun shone on the little brook.
   On the little brook, shone a bright sun.

2 A slight haze hung over the landscape.

3 The hills rose up majestically beyond the valley.

4 A rabbit appeared next to the oak tree.

5 The man stood between the field and the brook.

6 A young girl waited beside the bushes.

Reported speech

When the sisters talk together, they sometimes report things that other people have said to them. Look at these examples from the story. Anne is talking to Frances about Tom.

> *He reckoned he'd take me to Ollerton feast.*
> *And I told him I should tell you – an' I have done.*
> *No, he hasn't, when he'd said he'd take me.*

5 Now answer the questions:

1 Which word could Anne have used after *reckoned*, *him* and *said*?
2 What is the full form of *he'd* in the first sentence?
3 Look at the second sentence. What did Anne actually say to Tom?
4 What are the full forms of *he'd* in the third sentence?

6 Write these sentences in reported speech. We have done the first one for you, as an example.

1 'I didn't want to go to the party. I only went because of John', she told him.
She told him that she hadn't wanted to go to the party, and that she had only gone because of John.

2 'Will you be wearing your best dress?' she asked her sister.

3 'There weren't many people here yesterday,' he told her.

4 'I've always wanted to visit this place, and now I have,' she sighed.

5 'I'll take you again, if that's what you want,' she told her friends.

6 'Do you understand what I'm saying?' the teacher asked his students.

Vocabulary

Dialect and colloquial speech

The story uses colloquial, and sometimes, ungrammatical language for speech, and more formal, and often, poetic language for the description of surroundings and nature. Anne and Tom, in particular, use non-standard English words and expressions. Anne uses the affectionate term *duck* when she talks to Anne. Tom uses the word *moudiwarp* to refer to the mole, a local word which even native speakers would have to guess from its context. They also use ungrammatical speech, especially verbs. Even the 'better spoken' Frances says, *I'd* **forgot** *that*, rather than *forgotten*.

7 **Find these sentences in the story. Try and understand their meaning from the context and then rewrite them in standard English. We have done the first one for you, as an example.**

1 *What's a matter?'*
 What's the matter?

2 *He gave me a wild rabbit what he'd caught.*

3 *Well, 'appen it doesn't.*

4 *She won't fret her fat over that.*

5 *I s'll take it home.*

6 *He's bit me!*

7 *Oh, aye! An' that got your rag out, did it?*

8 *Oh, what's up wi' it?*

9 *I don't know what you two's been jawing about, I'm sure.*

10 *Tom Smedley's a good deal better to my thinking than Jimmy.*

Multiple-clause sentences

One of the features of an authentic text is the great variety in sentence length. Some of the sentences in the story are very short – only three or four words long. They provide contrast and dramatic effect. For example:

It was a puff of wind.
There was silence.
He resisted it.

Other sentences are much longer and contain multiple-clauses. Look at the sentence below, which is taken from the story. It describes the view that the sisters have from one side of the brook. Lawrence was a painter as well as a writer, and he paints a picture in words of the landscape as it appears before us, starting with the nearest fields and moving across the land to the distant hills.

> Across the brook began the immense pattern of agriculture, white chequering of barley stubble, brown squares of wheat, khaki patches of pasture, red stripes of fallow, with the woodland and the tiny village dark like ornaments, leading away to the distance, right to the hills, where the check-pattern grew smaller and smaller, till, in the blackish haze of heat, far off, only the tiny white squares of barley stubble showed distinct.

8 Can you break the sentence up into shorter sentences? Use the words below to help you.

Across the brook began the immense pattern of agriculture.

There was the white chequering of barley stubble.

There were ....

There were ....

There were ....

The woodland and ....

The check-pattern ....

In the blackish haze of heat ....

9 What difference do shorter sentences make to the effect?

10 Look for more examples of longer sentences in the story. What are they about? What effect do they have?

You will find examples of multiple-clause sentences throughout your reading of authentic texts. In this story, you will see many examples. Sentences like this are usually used to create atmosphere, or to change the pace of the story. It can be very effective, but the length and complexity of the sentences can also be confusing. If you find multiple-clause sentences difficult, break down the longer sentences into shorter clauses, as you have done here – this will make it easier to understand.

Literary analysis

Plot

1 What are the main events in the story? Can you write a summary of the story in one sentence?
2 What do you think is the most important event? How does the story lead up to this event? What happens as a consequence of the event? Think of what happens to the mole, the meeting with Tom Smedley, and the final meeting between Frances and Tom.

3 How does Frances really feel about Tom? Is he really *second best*?
   Give reasons for your answers.
4 What does the story tell us about relationships between men and
   women?
5 The story is titled *Second Best*. Can you think of another title?

Character

6 What do you know about Anne and Frances? Think about their
   age, social class and relationship with each other. Choose three
   adjectives to describe each girl.
7 What do you know about Tom's appearance? What is Frances's
   opinion of Tom?
8 How is Tom's attitude towards Anne different from his attitude
   towards Frances?
9 Think about Jimmy Barrass. How is he different to Tom?
10 Do you think young women today have the same kind of reactions
   to events as Anne and Frances? How are they the same? How are
   they different?
11 What kind of relationship do Tom and Frances have now? What
   do you think it will be like in the future?

Narration

12 Think about the main events in the story? Is it a story about
   events? Or is it mostly about people's feelings?
13 Anne tells Frances about what Tom has been doing. What do we
   learn from her account of Tom's behaviour? What does it tell us
   about Tom, Frances, and Anne herself?
14 The narrative moves between conversation, description of nature,
   and people's reactions and feelings. Which of these narrative
   modes do you think dominates the story?
15 Think about the story from the time the mole first appears until
   it is killed. What do we learn about the mole, the characters, and
   life, through the description of the creature and what happens to
   it? Does the mole disappear from the narrative while the girls are
   talking about Jimmy?
16 How much direct information does Lawrence give us about Tom's
   reactions to Frances? And about Frances's reactions to Tom? Why
   do you think this is?
17 Imagine that the story is told by Anne, Frances or Tom. How do
   you think their accounts would differ?

Atmosphere

18 What kind of day is it in the story – think about the weather, what is happening, the characters' feelings? How does Lawrence communicate this? Think of his descriptions of the surroundings and the reactions of the two girls.

19 How does the atmosphere of the story change after the mole is killed?

20 How does Lawrence reflect this? Again, think of his descriptions of the countryside and the girls' movements and reactions.

Style

Poetic language

Lawrence was a poet and his use of language in the story reflects this.

Repetition

In the second paragraph on page 23, he uses the verb *plucked* twice; he also uses *nervous* and *nervously*.

21 Which character is Lawrence describing with these words? What effect does the repetition have? Find some more examples.

Use of two adjectives

Lawrence often uses two adjectives separated by a comma to describe people. For example, he describes Frances as *whimsical, spasmodic*; *nervous, desperate*; *slight, wilful*.

22 Are the pairs of adjectives similar or different?
Find some more examples to describe character.

Simile

Lawrence describes Frances's face as *calm as a mask*. He also uses simile to describe the countryside, for example, *the willows ... shook ....with a dazzling effect like diamonds*.

23 Find some more examples of simile in the text. What effect do they have?

Unusual collocations[86]

Lawrence puts words together in an unusual way. For example, he uses the expression *morning-still* to describe the countryside. He also says of Frances that *she did not poignantly care*, which is an unusual way of saying that 'she did not care very much'. This poetic language has various effects, causing the reader to slow down and think more carefully about the feelings and descriptions he writes about.

24 Are there any other expressions that seem to you unusual or poetic?

Conversation

Look at the conversation between Frances and Anne on pages 23–29. Try reading it aloud with a partner as far as *'Here, wait for me'*, cried Anne.

25 How does Lawrence break up the conversation?

26 Which adverbs and phrases does Lawrence use to describe Frances's conversation? Make a list (*petulantly, on the point of tears* and so on). What impression do these words create?

27 What differences are there between Anne's speech and Frances's? Think about the style and content of the girls' conversation.

28 Look at the conversation between Tom and the girls on pages 31–33. Is it always clear what they are saying to each other? How does Lawrence convey the tension between Tom and Frances?

29 Try reading the conversation aloud with someone else. Why are some words written in capital letters? What effect does this have?

30 Read the passage (on page 27) beginning: *After several dabbling attempts* … in which Anne picks up the mole. Is this an effective description? How does Lawrence achieve this?

31 Read the passage (on page 28) beginning: *She dropped him to the floor* … in which Anne kills the mole. What are Frances's feelings as the mole tries to escape? Do you identify with these feelings?

Guidance to the above literary terms, answer keys to all the exercises and activities, plus a wealth of other reading-practice material, can be found on the student's section of the Macmillan Readers website at:
www.macmillanenglish.com/readers.

86 words used together

Bliss

by Katherine Mansfield

About the author

Katherine Mansfield Beauchamp was born in 1888 in Wellington, New Zealand, into a middle-class family. Her father was an important and respected banker and businessman.

Mansfield said she was 'always writing' and her first work was published when she was nine years old. As a child she went to a school in Karori, a village in the hills outside the capital city of Wellington, later returning to the city itself. But she was a rebellious child, who thought New Zealand was too rural, old-fashioned and conservative. In 1903, she travelled to London, where she studied at Queen's College and wrote for the *College Magazine*. A fellow student described her as 'a girl of great vitality, impulsive and strong-willed'.

Mansfield returned to New Zealand in 1906, where she took up music and studied typing and bookkeeping[1]. But she was restless and unhappy, and in 1908, having persuaded her father to give her a yearly allowance of £100, she moved back to England. She never visited New Zealand again.

In England she went to literary parties but was not very impressed by them: 'Pretty rooms and pretty people, pretty coffee, and cigarettes out of a silver tankard ... I was wretched,' she remembered. And so, she devoted herself to writing and love.

Hurt by the end of an affair with a young violinist, Garnet Trowell, Mansfield made a sudden decision to marry George Bowden, a singing teacher. But she left him a few days after the wedding, returning to her relationship with Trowell. She travelled with his opera company, and became pregnant, but then separated from him again. Mansfield stayed with an old friend, Ida Baker, until her aunt arrived from New Zealand; she took Mansfield to Bavaria in Germany, where she hoped the famous waters there would calm her down. Mansfield's baby was stillborn[2].

Mansfield stayed in Germany, where she became interested in the work of the Russian writer, Anton Chekhov – much of his work focused

1 the job of recording an organisation's financial account
2 born dead

on the psychological conflicts of people's characters and relationships, a feature of her later writing. For now, she wrote satirical stories about German characters. In 1910, when she returned to England, these stories were published in the journal, *The New Age*. Later that year, a collection of her stories was published, under the title, *In a German Pension*.

Although her writing was going well, her health was not. Mansfield became ill, and she continued to suffer from poor health for the rest of her life.

In 1911, Mansfield met John Middleton Murry, a Socialist and former literary critic. They married in 1918. Mansfield co-edited and contributed to a series of journals. Until 1914, she published stories in *Rhythm* and *The Blue Review*. Mansfield and Murray became closely associated with other writers of the day such as D H Lawrence, Aldous Huxley and Virginia Woolf; these writers became known as 'The Bloomsbury Group'.

In 1915, Mansfield's younger brother Leslie was killed in the First World War. Mansfield was devastated[3] and began to look back to happy memories of her childhood. She wrote *Prelude*, one of her most famous stories, during this period. In the same year, Mansfield discovered she had tuberculosis[4].

In her last years, Mansfield spent a lot of time in southern France and Switzerland, trying out different treatments for tuberculosis. She felt close to death, and she wrote obsessively about her childhood. The stories in her most famous collection, *The Garden Party*, were written at this time. She died on January 9th, 1923, near Fontainebleau, France, at the age of 34.

Only three volumes of Mansfield's stories were published during her lifetime, but her influence on the development of the short story is notable. After her death, John Middleton Murry re-edited and published most of her writings.

About the story

The short story *Bliss* – which means 'a feeling of perfect happiness' – was first published in the *Literary Review* in 1918. It was included in the 1920 collection *Bliss and Other Stories*, which was first published in New York.

3 very shocked and upset
4 a serious infectious disease affecting your lungs

Background information

Middle-class life

The story is set in London in the second decade of the 20th century.

We are not told what Harry's profession is but he and his wife Bertha lead a comfortable, middle-class life. There are at least three servants: Mary, the nurse, and the cook. The attitude to children at the time was that they should be 'seen but not heard'. Bertha has a baby, but she does not see her much because the nurse – or nanny – looks after the child, and has control over when she sees her. Harry says that he never sees the baby and will not be interested in her until she *has a lover*. The family give dinner parties, and have holidays in foreign countries. They attend a *club* where they mix with people of similar background.

Literary London

Bertha and Harry have friends who are *modern, keen on social questions* and move in literary circles – mixing with other writers, actors and artists. Mr Norman Knight wants to start a theatre, his wife experiments with interior decoration, and Eddie Warren is a writer. The guests consider themselves to be *bohemian* – informal, relaxed, and free, compared with the *conventional* (ordinary, traditional) formality and stiffness of most of society. Mrs Norman Knight's clothes have attracted attention on the train and this gives her the chance to criticise the middle class and their lack of a sense of humour. She speaks of her desire to design an interior following a *fried-fish scheme*, which she obviously thinks is original but sounds crazy. Eddie Warren speaks about the play *Love in False Teeth* and enthuses wildly over the first line of a poem: 'Why must it always be tomato soup?'

We know that Katherine Mansfield went to a lot of literary gatherings when she was in England. She knew the Bloomsbury Group[5] – a group of painters, critics, and writers, including Virginia Woolf[6]. Some of these people were brilliant and talented, but Mansfield was often bored at the parties, and found many of the conversations empty and pointless.

---

5 a group of authors and artists who lived in or near London in the early 20th century, whose work influenced many areas of artistic and intellectual thinking, including economics, feminism, literature and art

6 an English writer of novels and essays, part of the Bloomsbury Group, famous for introducing a literary style called 'stream of consciousness'

Summary

It may help you to know something about what happens in the story before you read it. Don't worry, this summary does not tell you how the story ends!

At the beginning of the story, Bertha, a woman of thirty, is walking back to her house in London. She is very excited and feels like running, playing or laughing out loud, but convention prevents her from expressing her feelings.

The maid opens the door and Bertha asks her if the fruit has arrived. The maid replies that everything has come. Bertha looks at herself in the mirror and sees a woman with *trembling lips* and an *air of listening, waiting for something ... divine to happen*. She places the fruit in the bowls and begins to laugh. She recognises that she is almost *hysterical*.

Bertha runs upstairs to see her baby. The nurse ('Nanny') is giving the little girl her supper. She tells Bertha about her day with the baby. She is amused because the baby has pulled at a dog's ear in the park.

Bertha thinks it is dangerous to let her baby do that, but she does not dare say anything. She begs Nanny to let her finish feeding the baby. Nanny thinks that this is a bad idea, but reluctantly gives the baby to her mother and leaves the room. Bertha is pleased to be alone with her child. However, Nanny soon returns and tells Bertha that her husband is on the telephone.

Bertha runs downstairs and takes the call from Harry, her husband. He tells her to delay dinner by ten minutes because he is going to be late. Bertha tries to continue the conversation and communicate her special mood, but she fails.

Bertha is giving a dinner party for some friends. The guests are: the Norman Knights, a couple who have connections with the theatre and the world of interior decoration; a young man, Eddie Warren who has just published some poems, and Miss Pearl Fulton. Bertha had met Pearl at a club and found her beautiful and mysterious. She tells Harry about her, but he does not see any mystery – he says only that she is *cold like all blonde women*.

Bertha looks out into the garden where there is a pear tree in full bloom. She sees the beautiful tree as a symbol of her own life, and makes a list in her mind of everything that she has. Life is perfect.

Then suddenly her joy is replaced by tiredness and she has to *drag herself upstairs to dress.*

The Norman Knights arrive and tell the story of their train journey. Harry arrives a little later and runs straight upstairs. Miss Fulton is the last to arrive. Bertha takes her arm and is overcome by a strong emotion *that she does not know what to do with.*

The guests sit down to dinner and share gossip about people and the theatre. Bertha is filled with bliss and is more and more convinced that Miss Fulton and she experience the same sensations and feelings for each other.

Miss Fulton asks to see the garden, and Bertha interprets this as a sign that there is perfect understanding between them. They stand together at the window and look at the pear tree. Later, Bertha is upset to see that Harry seems to dislike Miss Fulton. She wonders how he can dislike someone who interests her so much, and decides to tell Harry that night about how much she likes Miss Fulton.

Bertha realises that *for the first time in her life* that she desires her husband. She has always accepted that her husband is *different*, but they have been *such good pals* (friends) that it did not seem to matter – although her own coldness had been a worry to her at first. She finds comfort in the fact that she and her husband have always been *frank* (honest) with each other and share a *modern* relationship.

The guests prepare to leave. Miss Fulton moves towards the hall and Harry pushes past Bertha with an offer to *help* Miss Fulton with her coat. Bertha thinks that he is sorry for his earlier rudeness and wants to behave better. She moves towards a table opposite the drawing-room door where there is a book that Eddie is interested in. While he looks at the book, Bertha turns her head towards the hall and sees something quite unexpected…

Pre-reading exercises

Key vocabulary

This section will help you familiarise yourself with some of the more specific vocabulary used in the story. You may want to use it to help you before you start reading, or as a revision exercise after you have finished the story.

The descriptions of the pear tree

The pear tree appears several times in the story. Read the descriptions below.

> a) *At the far end, against the wall, there was a tall, slender pear tree in fullest, richest bloom; it stood perfect, as though becalmed against the jade-green sky.*
>
> b) *And she seemed to see on her eyelids the lovely pear tree with its wide open blossoms as a symbol of her own life.*
>
> c) *And still, in the back of her mind, there was the pear tree. It would be silver now, in the light of poor dear Eddie's moon, silver as Miss Fulton...*
>
> d) *And the two women stood side by side looking at the slender, flowering tree. Although it was so still it seemed, like the flame of a candle, to stretch up, to point, to quiver in the bright air, to grow taller as they gazed – almost to touch the rim of the round, silver moon.*
>
> e) *But the pear tree was as lovely as ever and as full of flower and as still.*

1 Now answer the questions.

1 Which adjective, used twice, means 'thin and graceful'?
2 What other adjectives are used to describe the tree? Make a list: *tall,...*
3 Which phrases tell us that the tree is in flower?
4 What is the tree compared to in (D)?
5 Which words suggest that the tree is not moving?
6 Which verbs suggest that the tree may be moving slightly?

Adjectives

2 The story is told from Bertha's single point of view. Look at the adjectives used to describe her emotions and responses, and then use the words to complete the passage below.

> absurd trembling hysterical ardent tender radiant
> unbearable child-like

Bertha is overcome by a feeling of bliss which is almost
(1 ....), or **too much to bear**. Her face in the mirror is
shining, (2 ....), and her lips are **moving slightly
with emotion** (3 ....) She wants to laugh aloud
for no reason and feels that she is becoming **out of control** or
(4 ....) It seems **ridiculous** or (5 ....
) to her that she bought purple grapes to match the dining-room
carpet. At dinner, Harry praises the dessert and Bertha is filled with
innocent, (6 ....) pleasure. She looks around at her
guests and feels **warm and affectionate,** or (7 ....)
towards them. That evening, for the first time, Bertha has **passionate,**
(8 ....) feelings for her husband.

Describing colour

There is an emphasis on colour in the story. It is usually used in
connection with what people are wearing and eating; it shows how
much the characters are interested in how they look.

**3 Look at the phrases below. Classify them into *clothes and
jewellery,* or *food.***

> yellow silk dress
> apples stained with strawberry pink
> white grapes covered with a silver bloom
> little red flannel jacket
> white dress, a string of jade beads, green shoes and stockings
> a silver fillet binding her pale blonde hair
> the green of pistachio ices
> beautiful red soup in the grey plate
> amber ear-rings
> a big cluster of purple ones
> the most amusing orange coat
> a procession of black monkeys around the hem
> white flesh of the lobster
> yellow pears, smooth as silk
> a white flannel gown and a blue woollen jacket

4 Now answer the questions below:

1 Which verb means 'marked with another colour'?
2 What are silk, flannel and wool all types of .... ?
3 What colour is *jade*? What are *beads*?
4 Which word is used to describe a lot of grapes on the same stem?
5 Where is the *hem* of something usually found?
6 What colour is *amber*?
7 What do you think a *fillet* is?
8 What kind of seafood is mentioned?
9 What colour do you think the *ices* are?

Main themes

Before you read the story, you may want to think about some of its main themes. The questions will help you think about the story as you are reading it for the first time. There is more discussion of the main themes in the *Literary analysis* section after the story.

Different kinds of love

There are lots of different kinds of love in this story. We are told that Bertha regularly 'falls in love' with young, beautiful women but this seems to mean admiring them from a distance; we learn that Bertha loves Harry and that they are good friends, as well as husband and wife. However, Bertha does not love Harry *in that way*. At first, she was worried to find that she was so cold, but she has now got used to the situation.

At the time of the story, Bertha is fascinated by Pearl. However, during the course of the evening, she becomes more interested in Harry, and for the first time, Bertha *desires* him. Is it because she has sensed the attraction between Pearl and Harry?

5 As you read the story, ask yourself:

a) Is Bertha hysterical?
b) Is Bertha a *cold* person?
c) What evidence can you give for your answers?

Individual perception

At the time the story was written there was a lot of interest in psychoanalysis[7] and the subconscious[8]. Everything in the story is seen from Bertha's point of view.

6 As you read the story, ask yourself:

a) How much does Bertha 'know' and how much does she 'feel'?
b) Does she 'know' herself?
c) Is Bertha right in her assessment of other people?

Life versus 'civilisation'

Mansfield seems to be saying that life is full of messy relationships, while *civilisation* is something completely different, unreal, and often ridiculous, or *absurd*.

Bertha says, *How idiotic civilization is!* because she can't run and dance in the street because if she does, people will think that she is drunk. She asks herself: *Why be given a body if you have to keep it shut up in a case like a rare, rare fiddle?*

And later, in the nursery, when the Nanny does not want to give her baby to her, she thinks: *How absurd it was. Why have a baby if it has to be kept – not in a case like a rare, rare fiddle – but in another woman's arms?*

Again, after she has failed to communicate her feelings to her husband on the phone, she hangs up, *thinking how much more than idiotic civilization was.*

7 As you read the story, think about the following:

a) How much control has Bertha got over her own life?
b) How is she treated by the Nanny, her husband, and the guests at the dinner party?

7 medical treatment in which someone talks to a psychoanalyst about their feelings in order to understand their own behaviour better, or to solve their mental problems
8 the part of your mind that contains thoughts and feelings that you do not think about, or do not realise you have

Bliss

by Katherine Mansfield

Although Bertha Young was thirty she still had moments like this when she wanted to run instead of walk, to take dancing steps on and off the pavement, to bowl a hoop[9], to throw something up in the air and catch it again, or to stand still and laugh at – nothing – at nothing, simply.

What can you do if you are thirty and, turning the corner of your own street, you are overcome, suddenly, by a feeling of **bliss** – absolute bliss! – as though you'd suddenly swallowed a bright piece of that late afternoon sun and it burned in your bosom[10], sending out a little shower of sparks into every particle, into every finger and toe? ...

Oh, is there no way you can express it without being 'drunk and disorderly'[11]? How **idiotic** civilization is! Why be given a body if you have to keep it shut up in a case like a rare, rare fiddle[12]?

'No, that about the fiddle is not quite what I mean,' she thought, running up the steps and feeling in her bag for the key – she'd forgotten it, as usual – and **rattling** the letterbox. 'It's not what I mean, because – thank you, Mary' – she went into the hall. 'Is nurse[13] back?'

'Yes, M'm[14].'

'And has the fruit come?'

'Yes, M'm. Everything's come.'

'Bring the fruit up to the dining-room, will you? I'll arrange it before I go upstairs.'

---

9 to roll a large ring along the ground; an old-fashioned child's game
10 *mainly literary, old-fashioned*: a woman's chest, or the clothes covering it
11 to be noisy and violent in a public place because you are drunk; this is an offence in the UK
12 *colloquial*: violin
13 *old-fashioned*: woman whose job it is to look after a young child; also 'nanny'
14 *abbreviation*: Madam

It was dusky[15] in the dining-room and quite **chilly**. But all the same Bertha threw off her coat; she could not bear the tight clasp[16] of it another moment, and the cold air fell on her arms.

But in her bosom there was still that bright glowing place – that shower of little sparks coming from it. It was almost **unbearable**. She hardly dared to breathe for fear of fanning it higher, and yet she breathed deeply, deeply. She hardly dared to look into the cold mirror – but she did look, and it gave her back a woman, **radiant**, with smiling, trembling lips, with big, dark eyes and an air of listening, waiting for something … divine[17] to happen … that she knew must happen … **infallibly**.

Mary brought in the fruit on a tray and with it a glass bowl, and a blue dish, very lovely, with a strange sheen[18] on it as though it had been dipped in milk.

'Shall I turn on the light, M'm?'

'No, thank you. I can see quite well.'

There were tangerines[19] and apples stained with strawberry pink. Some yellow pears, smooth as silk, some white grapes covered with a silver bloom and a big cluster of purple ones. These last she had bought to tone in with the new dining-room carpet. Yes, that did sound rather **far-fetched** and **absurd**, but it was really why she had bought them. She had thought in the shop: 'I must have some purple ones to bring the carpet up to the table.' And it had seemed quite sense[20] at the time.

When she had finished with them and had made two **pyramids** of these bright round shapes, she stood away from the table to get the effect – and it really was most curious[21]. For the dark table seemed to melt into the dusky light and the glass dish and the blue bowl to **float** in the air. This, of course, in her present mood, was so incredibly beautiful … She began to laugh.

---

15 not very bright, because of shadows or because night is coming
16 *mainly literary:* way of holding something tightly
17 *informal, old-fashioned:* extremely good or pleasant
18 a shine on the surface of something
19 a fruit similar to a small orange but with loose skin that is more easily removed
20 it made sense/seemed reasonable
21 unusual and interesting (when used to describe a thing)

'No, no. I'm getting hysterical.' And she seized her bag and coat and ran upstairs to the nursery.

Nurse sat at a low table giving Little B her supper after her bath. The baby had on a white flannel[22] gown and a blue woollen jacket, and her dark, fine hair was brushed up into a funny little peak[23]. She looked up when she saw her mother and began to jump.

'Now, my lovey[24], eat it up like a good girl,' said Nurse, setting her lips in a way that Bertha knew, and that meant she had come into the nursery at another wrong moment.

'Has she been good, Nanny?'

'She's been a little sweet all the afternoon,' whispered Nanny. 'We went to the park and I sat down on a chair and took her out of the pram and a big dog came along and put its head on my knee and she clutched its ear, **tugged** it. Oh, you should have seen her.'

Bertha wanted to ask if it wasn't rather dangerous to let her clutch at a strange dog's ear. But she did not dare to. She stood watching them, her hands by her side, like the poor little girl in front of the rich little girl with the doll.

The baby looked up at her again, stared, and then smiled so **charmingly** that Bertha couldn't help crying:

'Oh, Nanny, do let me finish giving her her supper while you put the bath things away.'

'Well, M'm she oughtn't to be changed hands while she's eating,' said Nanny, still whispering. 'It unsettles her; it's very likely to upset her.'

How absurd it was. Why have a baby if it has to kept – not in a case like a rare, rare fiddle – but in another woman's arms?

'Oh, I must!' she said.

Very **offended**, Nanny handed her over.

'Now, don't excite her after her supper. You know you do, M'm. And I have such a time with her after!'

Thank heaven! Nanny went out of the room with the bath towels.

22 soft cotton cloth used for making clothes and sheets
23 an object or shape that looks like the top of a mountain
24 *informal*: 'dear'

'Now I've got you to myself, my little **precious**,' said Bertha, as the baby leaned against her.

She ate delightfully, holding up her lips for the spoon and then waving her hands. Sometime she wouldn't let the spoon go; and sometimes, just as Bertha had filled it, she waved it away to the four winds[25].

When the soup was finished Bertha turned round to the fire.

'You're nice – you've very nice!' she said, kissing her warm baby. 'I'm fond[26] of you. I like you.'

And, indeed, she loved Little B so much – her neck as she bent forward, her exquisite toes as they shone **transparent** in the firelight – that all her feeling of bliss came back again, and again she didn't know how to express it – what to do with it.

'You're wanted on the telephone,' said Nanny, coming back in triumph and seizing *her* Little B.

Down she flew. It was Harry.

'Oh, is that you, Ber? Look here. I'll be late. I'll take a taxi and come along as quickly as I can, but get dinner put back ten minutes – will you? All right?'

'Yes, perfectly. Oh, Harry!'

'Yes?'

What had she to say? She'd nothing to say. She only wanted to get in touch with him for a moment. She couldn't absurdly cry: 'Hasn't it been a **divine** day!'

'What is it?' rapped out the little voice.

'Nothing. *Entendu*[27]' said Bertha, and hung up the receiver, thinking how more than idiotic civilization was.

They had people coming to dinner. The Norman Knights – a very sound[28] couple – he was about to start a theatre, and she was awfully keen on interior decoration, a young man, Eddie Warren, who had just published a little book of poems and whom everybody was asking to dine, and a 'find' of Bertha's called Pearl Fulton. What Miss Fulton did, Bertha didn't know. They had

25 *literary, phrase 'to the four winds'*: to make a group of things or people become separated from each other and lost
26 liking or caring about someone very much
27 *French*: 'understood'
28 *formal*: reliable and sensible

met at the club and Bertha had fallen in love with her, as she always did fall in love with beautiful women who had something strange about them.

The **provoking** thing was that, though they had been about together and met a number of times and really talked, Bertha couldn't yet make her out. Up to a certain point Miss Fulton was rarely, wonderfully **frank**, but the certain point was there, and beyond that she would not go.

Was there anything beyond it? Harry said 'No.' Voted her dullish, and 'cold like all blonde women, with a touch, perhaps, of anaemia[29] of the brain'. But Bertha wouldn't agree with him; not yet, at any rate.

'No, the way she has of sitting with her head a little on one side, and smiling, has something behind it, Harry, and I must find out what that something is.'

'Most likely it's a good stomach,' answered Harry.

He made a point of catching Bertha's heels[30] with replies of that kind ... 'liver frozen, my dear girl', or 'pure flatulence[31]', or 'kidney disease', ... and so on. For some strange reason Bertha liked this, and almost admired it in him very much.

She went into the drawing-room and lighted the fire; then picking up the cushions, one by one, that Mary had disposed so carefully, she threw them back on to the chairs and the **couches**. That made all the difference; the room came alive at once. As she was about to throw the last one she surprised herself by suddenly **hugging** it to her, passionately, passionately. But it did not put out the fire in her bosom. Oh, on the contrary!

The windows of the drawing-room opened on to a balcony overlooking the garden. At the far end, against the wall, there was a tall, **slender** pear tree in fullest, richest **bloom**; it stood perfect, as though becalmed against the jade-green sky. Bertha couldn't help feeling, even from this distance, that it had not a single bud or a faded petal. Down below, in the garden beds, the red and yellow tulips, heavy with flowers, seemed to lean upon

29 a medical condition in which your blood contains too few red blood cells
30 *very unusual:* surprise someone, take someone off their guard
31 too much gas in your stomach or intestines

the dusk. A grey cat, dragging its belly, crept across the lawn, and a black one, its shadow, trailed after. The sight of them, so intent and so quick, gave Bertha a curious shiver.

'What **creepy** things cats are!' she stammered, and she turned away from the window and began walking up and down …

How strong the jonquils[32] smelled in the warm room. Too strong? Oh no. And yet, as though overcome, she flung down on a couch and pressed her hands to her eyes.

'I'm too happy – too happy!' she murmured.

And she seemed to see on her eyelids the lovely pear tree with its wide open blossoms as a symbol of her own life.

Really – really – she had everything. She was young. Harry and she were as much in love as ever, and they got on together splendidly and were really good pals. She had an adorable baby. They didn't have to worry about money. They had this absolutely satisfactory house and garden. And friends – modern, thrilling friends, writers and painters and poets or people keen on social questions – just the kind of friends they wanted. And then there were books, and there was music, and she had found a wonderful little dressmaker, and they were going abroad in the summer, and their new cook made the most superb omelettes,…

'I'm absurd. Absurd!' She sat up; but she felt quite **dizzy**, quite drunk. It must have been the spring.

Yes, it was the spring. Now she was so tired she could not drag herself upstairs to dress.

A white dress, a string of jade beads, green shoes and stockings. It wasn't intentional. She had thought of this **scheme** hours before she stood at the drawing-room window.

Her **petals** rustled softly into the hall, and she kissed Mrs Norman Knight, who was taking off the most amusing orange coat with a procession of black monkeys around the hem and up the fronts.

'… Why! Why! Why is the middle-class so stodgy – so utterly without a sense of humour! My dear, it's only by a **fluke** that I am here at all – Norman being the protective fluke. For my darling monkeys so upset the train that it rose to a man and

32 a kind of flower

simply ate me with its eyes. Didn't laugh – wasn't amused – that I should have loved. No, just stared – and bored me through and through.'

'But the cream[33] of it was,' said Norman, pressing a large tortoiseshell[34]-rimmed monocle[35] into his eye, 'you don't mind me telling this, Face, do you?' (In their home and among their friends they called each other Face and Mug.) 'The cream of it was when she, being full fed[36], turned to the woman beside her and said: 'Haven't you ever seen a monkey before?''

'Oh, yes!' Mrs Norman Knight joined in the laughter. 'Wasn't that too absolutely creamy?'

And a funnier thing still was that now her coat was off she did look like a very intelligent monkey – who had even made that yellow silk dress out of scraped banana skins. And her amber ear-rings; they were like little dangling nuts.

'This is a sad, sad fall!' said Mug, pausing in front of Little B's perambulator. 'When the perambulator[37] comes into the hall – ' and he waved the rest of the quotation away.

The bell rang. It was lean, pale Eddie Warren (as usual) in a state of **acute** distress.

'It *is* the right house, *isn't* it?' he pleaded.

'Oh, I think so – I hope so,' said Bertha brightly.

'I have had such a *dreadful* experience with a taxi-man; he was *most* sinister. I couldn't get him to *stop*. The *more* I knocked and called the *faster* he went. And *in* the moonlight the **bizarre** figure with the *flattened* head **crouching** over the *lit-tle* wheel….'

He shuddered, taking off an immense white silk scarf. Bertha noticed that his socks were white, too – most charming.

'But how dreadful!' she cried.

'Yes, it really was,' said Eddie, following her into the drawing-room. 'I saw myself *driving* through Eternity in a *timeless* taxi.'

He knew the Norman Knights. In fact, he was going to write a play for N. K. when the theatre scheme came off.

33 the best part
34 made of the hard shell of a type of turtle that is brown and orange
35 a glass lens for one eye, used in the past to help you see better
36 *unusual:* when you have reached the limits of your patience
37 the full form of 'pram', a carriage with wheels for a baby

'Well, Warren, how's the play?' said Norman Knight, dropping his monocle and giving his eyes a moment in which to rise to the surface before it was screwed down again.

And Mrs Norman Knight: 'Oh, Mr Warren, what happy socks?'

'I *am* so glad you like them,' sad he, staring at his feet. 'They seem to have got so *much* whiter since the moon rose.' And he turned his lean sorrowful young face to Bertha. 'There *is* a moon, you know.'

She wanted to cry: 'I am sure there is – often – often!'

He really was a most attractive person. But so was Face, crouched before the fire in her banana skins, and so was Mug, smoking a cigarette and saying as he **flicked** the ash: 'Why doth the bridegroom tarry[38]?'

'There he is, now.'

Bang went the front door open and shut. Harry shouted: 'Hullo, you people. Down in five minutes.' And they heard him **swarm** up the stairs. Bertha couldn't help smiling; she knew how he loved doing things at high pressure. What, after all, did an extra five minutes matter? But he would pretend to himself that they mattered beyond measure. And then he would make a great point of coming into the drawing-room, **extravagantly** cool and collected.

Harry had such a zest[39] for life. Oh, how she appreciated it in him. And his passion for fighting – for seeking in everything that came up against him another test of his power and of his courage – that, too, she understood. Even when it made him just occasionally, to other people, who didn't know him well, a little **ridiculous** perhaps ... For there were moments when he rushed into battle where no battle was ... She talked and laughed and positively forgot until he had come in (just as she had imagined) that Pearl Fulton had not turned up.

'I wonder if Miss Fulton has forgotten?'

'I expect so,' said Harry. 'Is she on the phone?'

'Ah! There's a taxi, now.' And Bertha smiled with that little

38 *literary question:* Why is the bridegroom late?
39 great enthusiasm or interest

air of proprietorship that she always assumed while her women finds were new and mysterious. 'She lives in taxis.'

'She'll run to fat[40] if she does,' said Harry coolly, ringing the bell for dinner. 'Frightful danger for blonde women.'

'Harry – don't,' warned Bertha, laughing up at him.

Came another tiny moment, while they waited, laughing and talking, just a trifle[41] too much at their ease, a trifle too unaware. And then Miss Fulton, all in silver, with a silver fillet[42] binding her pale blonde hair, came in smiling, her head a little on one side.

'Am I late?'

'No, not at all,' said Bertha. 'Come along.' And she took her arm and they moved into the dining-room.

What was there in the touch of that cool arm that could fan – fan – start blazing[43] – blazing – the fire of bliss that Bertha did not know what to do with?

Miss Fulton did not look at her; but then she **seldom** did look at people directly. Her heavy eyelids lay upon her eyes and the strange half smile came and went upon her lips as though she lived by listening rather than seeing. But Bertha knew, suddenly, as if the longest, most intimate look had passed between them – as if they had said to each other: 'You, too?' – that Pearl Fulton, stirring the beautiful red soup in the grey plate, was feeling just what she was feeling.

And the others? Face and Mug, Eddie and Harry, their spoons rising and falling – dabbing their lips with their napkins, **crumbling** bread, fiddling with the forks and glasses and talking.

'I met her at the Alpha show – the weirdest little person. She'd not only cut off her hair, but she seemed to have taken a dreadfully good slip[44] off her legs and arms and her neck and her poor little nose as well.'

40 *colloquial, old-fashioned:* to get fat
41 *formal, old-fashioned:* slightly
42 *old-fashioned:* a band or ribbon for the hair
43 *mainly literary:* burning strongly, brightly (usually refers to fire)
44 cut

'Isn't she very *liee*[45] with Michael Oat?'

'The man who wrote *Love in False Teeth?*'

'He wants to write a play for me. One act. One man. Decides to commit suicide. Gives all the reasons why he should and why he shouldn't. And just as he has made up his mind either to do it or not to do it – curtain. Not half a bad idea.'

'What's he going to call it – 'Stomach Trouble'?'

'I *think* I've come across the *same* idea in a lit-tle French review, *quite* unknown in England.'

No, they didn't share it. They were dears – dears – and she loved having them there, at her table, and giving them delicious food and wine. In fact, she longed to tell them how delightful they were, and what a decorative group they made, how they seemed to set one another off and how they reminded her of a play by Chekhov[46].

Harry was enjoying his dinner. It was part of his – well, not his nature, exactly, and certainly not his pose – his – something or other – to talk about food and to glory in his 'shameless passion for the white flesh of the lobster' and ' the green of pistachio ices – green and cold like the eyelids of Egyptian dancers'.

When he looked up at her and said: 'Bertha, this is a very admirable *soufflé*[47]!' she almost could have **wept** with child-like pleasure.

Oh, why did she feel so tender towards the whole world tonight? Everything was good – was right. All that happened seemed to fill again her brimming cup of bliss.

And still, in the back of her mind, there was the pear tree. It would be silver now, in the light of poor dear Eddie's moon, silver as Miss Fulton, who sat there turning a tangerine in her slender fingers that were so pale a light seemed to come from them.

What she simply couldn't make out – what was **miraculous** – was how she should have guessed Miss Fulton's mood so exactly and so instantly. For she never doubted for a moment that she

45 *French:* having an affair with
46 19th century Russian writer who was a keen observer of human behaviour
47 a food that you make with eggs and bake into a high round shape

was right, and yet what had she to go on? Less than nothing.

'I believe this does happen very, very rarely between women. Never between men,' thought Bertha. 'But while I am making the coffee in the drawing-room perhaps she will 'give a sign'.'

What she meant by that she did not know, and what would happen after that she could not imagine.

While she thought like this she saw herself talking and laughing. She had to talk because of her desire to laugh.

'I must laugh or die.'

But when she noticed Face's funny little habit of tucking[48] something down the front of her bodice[49] – as if she kept a tiny, secret hoard of nuts there, too – Bertha had to dig her nails into her hands – so as not to laugh too much.

It was over at last. And: 'Come and see my new coffee machine,' said Bertha.

'We only have a new coffee machine once a fortnight,' said Harry. Face took her arm this time; Miss Fulton bent her head and followed after.

The fire had died down in the drawing-room to a red, flickering 'nest of baby phoenixes[50]', said Face.

'Don't turn up the light for a moment. It is so lovely.'

And down she crouched by the fire again. She was always cold … 'without her little red flannel jacket, of course,' thought Bertha.

At that moment Miss Fulton 'gave the sign'.

'Have you a garden?' said the cool, sleepy voice.

This was so exquisite on her part that all Bertha could do was to obey. She crossed the room, pulled the curtains apart, and opened those long windows.

'There!' she breathed.

And the two women stood side by side looking at the slender, flowering tree. Although it was so still it seemed, like the flame of a candle, to stretch up, to point, to quiver in the bright air, to

48 to put the end of a piece of clothing under or behind another piece in order to keep it tidy
49 the part of a dress that covers a woman's body from the waist up
50 an imaginary bird in ancient stories that lives for 500 years and then burns to death, with a new phoenix rising from the ashes when the flames are gone

grow taller as they gazed – almost to touch the rim of the round, silver moon.

How long did they stand there? Both, as it were, caught in that circle of unearthly light, understanding each other perfectly, creatures of another world, and wondering what they were to do in this one with all this blissful treasure that burned in their bosoms and dropped, in silver flowers, from their hair and hands?

For ever – for a moment? And did Miss Fulton murmur : 'Yes.' Just *that?* Or did Bertha dream it?

Then the light was snapped on and Face made the coffee and Harry said: 'My dear Mrs Knight, don't ask me about my baby. I never see her. I shan't feel the slightest interest in her until she has a lover,' and Mug took his eye out of the conservatory[51] for a moment and then put it under glass again and Eddie Warren drank his coffee and set down the cup with a face of **anguish** as though he had drunk and seen the spider[52].

'What I want to do is to give the young men a show. I believe London is simply **teeming** with first-chop[53], unwritten plays. What I want to say to 'em is: 'Here's the theatre. Fire ahead."

'You know, my dear, I am going to decorate a room for the Jacob Nathans. Oh, I am so tempted to do a fried-fish scheme, with the backs of the chairs shaped like frying pans and lovely chip potatoes embroidered all over the curtains.'

'The trouble with our young writing men is that they are still too romantic. You can't put out to sea without being seasick and wanting a basin. Well, why won't they have the courage of those basins?'

'A *dreadful* poem about a *girl* who was *violated*[54] by a beggar[55] *without* a nose in a lit-tle wood…'

Miss Fulton sank into the lowest, deepest chair and Harry handed round the cigarettes.

51 a room with glass walls and a glass roof, built next to a house and used for relaxing in or for growing plants
52 reference to Shakespeare's play, *The Winters Tale*, act 2, sc. I, l. 45
53 first-time writers
54 *old-fashioned:* to rape someone
55 someone who is very poor and lives by asking people for money or food

From the way he stood in front of her shaking the silver box and saying abruptly: 'Egyptian? Turkish? Virginian? They're all mixed up,' Bertha realized that she not only bored him; he really disliked her. And she decided from the way Miss Fulton said: 'No, thank you, I won't smoke,' that she felt it, too, and was hurt.

'Oh, Harry, don't dislike her. You are quite wrong about her. She's wonderful, wonderful. And, besides, how can you feel so differently about someone who means so much to me. I shall try to tell you when we are in bed tonight what has been happening. What she and I have shared.'

At those last words something strange and almost terrifying darted into Bertha's mind. And this something blind and smiling whispered to her: 'Soon these people will go. The house will be quiet – quiet. The lights will be out. And you and he will be alone together in the dark room – the warm bed....'

She jumped from her chair and ran over to the piano.

'What a pity someone does not play!' she cried. 'What a pity somebody does not play.'

For the first time in her life Bertha Young desired her husband.

Oh, she'd loved him – she'd been in love with him, of course, in every other way, but just not in that way. And, equally, of course, she'd understood that he was different. They'd discussed it so often. It had worried her dreadfully at first to find that she was so cold, but after a time it had not seemed to matter. They were so frank with each other – such good pals. That was the best of being modern.

But now – **ardently**! Ardently! The word ached in her ardent body! Was this what that feeling of bliss had been leading up to? But then –

'My dear,' said Mrs Norman Knight, 'you know our shame. We are **victims** of time and train. We live in Hampstead. It's been so nice.'

'I'll come with you into the hall,' said Bertha. 'I loved having you. But you must not miss the last train. That's so awful, isn't it?'

'Have a whisky, Knight, before you go?' called Harry.

'No thanks, old chap.'

Bertha squeezed his hand for that as she shook it.

'Good night, good-bye,' she cried from the top step, feeling that this self of hers was taking leave of them for ever.

When she got back into the drawing-room the others were on the move.

'...Then you can come part of the way in my taxi.'

'I shall be *so* thankful *not* to have to face *another* drive *alone* after my **dreadful** experience.'

'You can get a taxi at the **rank** just at the end of the street. You won't have to walk more than a few yards.'

'That's a comfort. I'll go and put on my coat.'

Miss Fulton moved towards the hall and Bertha was following when Harry almost pushed past.

'Let me help you.'

Bertha knew that he was repenting his rudeness – she let him go. What a boy he was in some ways – so **impulsive** – so – simple.

And Eddie and she were left by the fire.

'I *wonder* if you have seen Bilks' *new* poem called *Table d'Hote,*' said Eddie softly. 'It's *so* wonderful. In the last anthology. Have you got a copy? I'd *so* like to *show* it to you. It begins with an *incredibly* beautiful line: 'Why must it always be tomato soup?"

'Yes,' said Bertha. And she moved noiselessly to a table opposite the drawing-room door and Eddie **glided** noiselessly after her. She picked up the little book and gave it to him; they had not made a sound.

While he looked it up she turned her head towards the hall. And she saw ... Harry with Miss Fulton's coat in his arms and Miss Fulton with her back turned to him and her head bent. He tossed the coat away, put his hands on her shoulders, and turned her violently to him. His lips said: 'I adore you,' and Miss Fulton laid her moonbeam fingers on his cheeks and smiled her sleepy smile. Harry's nostrils quivered; his lips curled back in a **hideous grin** while he whispered: 'Tomorrow,' and with her eyelids Miss Fulton said: 'Yes.'

'Here it is,' said Eddie. "Why must it always be tomato soup?" It's so *deeply* true, don't you feel? Tomato soup is so *dreadfully* eternal.'

'If you prefer,' said Harry's voice, very loud, from the hall, 'I can phone you a cab to come to the door.'

'Oh, no. It's not necessary,' said Miss Fulton, and she came up to Bertha and gave her the slender fingers to hold.

'Good-bye. Thank you so much.'

'Good-bye,' said Bertha.

Miss Fulton held her hand a moment longer.

'Your lovely pear tree!' she murmured.

And then she was gone, with Eddie following, like the black cat following the grey cat.

'I'll shut up shop[56]', said Harry, extravagantly cool and collected.

'Your lovely pear tree – pear tree – pear tree!'

Bertha simply ran over to the long windows.

'Oh, what is going to happen now?' she cried.

But the pear tree was as lovely as ever and as full of flower and as still.

---

56 *colloquial*: to lock the doors and secure the house or office/business before going to bed/leaving

Post-reading exercises

Understanding the story

1 **Use these questions to check that you have understood the story.**

In the street
1 Where is Bertha going at the beginning of the story?
2 How does she feel?
3 Is it the first time she has felt like this? How do you know?

The arrival home
4 Who is Mary?
5 What does Bertha ask Mary to do?
6 Why has Bertha bought purple grapes?
7 How does she feel after she has arranged the fruit?

In the nursery
8 Why does Bertha go to the nursery?
9 What is Nanny's reaction to Bertha's arrival?
10 What did the baby do in the park? How does Bertha feel about this?
11 How would you describe Bertha's relationship with Nanny?
12 How does Bertha feel about her baby? What words does she use?

The phone call
13 Why does Harry phone Bertha?
14 How would you describe their conversation?

The dinner guests
15 Who is coming to dinner?
16 What kind of work do they do?
17 Who is Pearl Fulton and how does Bertha feel about her?
18 What does Harry say about Pearl?

Before the guests arrive
19 What does Bertha do with the cushions?
20 What does she see in the garden?
21 How is the pear tree a *symbol of her own life*?
22 Why does Bertha consider that she has *everything*?
23 How does Bertha explain her sudden tiredness?

The first guests arrive
24 What do the Norman Knights call each other?
25 What happened to them on the train?
26 Why is Eddie Warren in a state of *acute distress*?

Harry's arrival

27 Where does Harry go when he arrives home?
28 What is Bertha's attitude to his late arrival?

Pearl's arrival

29 How does Bertha feel when she takes Pearl's arm?
30 Do we know what Pearl is feeling?

The dinner

31 How would you describe the conversation at the dinner table?
32 Do we know what Bertha and Pearl say?
33 What do you understand by the phrase: *It was over at last.*? What
    does this tell us about how Bertha felt about the dinner party?

Pearl, Bertha and the garden

34 How does Bertha interpret Pearl's question: *Have you a garden?*
35 How does Bertha feel while they look at the pear tree together?
    And Pearl?

Coffee time

36 What is the conversation about over coffee? Who speaks most?
37 What does Harry offer Pearl?
38 How does Bertha interpret Harry's attitude to Pearl?
39 What does Bertha decide to tell Harry that night?
40 What happens to Bertha *for the first time in her life*?
41 What do you think Bertha and Harry's marriage is like?

The guests leave

42 Which guests are going to share a taxi?
43 Why does Pearl move into the hall?
44 Why does Harry follow her?
45 What does Bertha see in the hall?
46 How do you think she feels?
47 What is the significance of the last sentence?

Language study

Grammar

The use of auxiliary verbs to create emphasis

One way of creating emphasis is to use an auxiliary verb such as *do*
or *did* in sentences where it is not strictly necessary. Look at these
examples from the story. Notice how the language helps to emphasise
Bertha's changing moods and feelings.

> *She hardly dared look into the cold mirror – but she did look.*
> *She had bought (the grapes) to tone in with the new dining-room carpet.*
> *Yes, that did sound rather far-fetched and absurd, but it was really why she*
> *had bought them.*
> *'Oh, Nanny, do let me finish giving her her supper...'*
> *Bertha had fallen in love with her, as she always did fall in love with*
> *beautiful women who had something strange about them.*
> *Miss Fulton did not look at her; but then she seldom did look at people*
> *directly.*
> *'I believe this does happen very, very rarely between women.'*

1 Now answer the questions.

1 In which sentence is Bertha trying to persuade someone?

2 In which sentence does Bertha seem to be having an argument with herself?

2 Make these sentences more emphatic by using an auxiliary verb. We have done the first one for you, as an example.

1 He didn't want to attend the dinner party but he went in the end.
   He didn't want to attend the dinner party but he did go in the end.

2 Oh, be careful with the baby, or you'll drop her!

3 Sam looks smart today, don't you think?

4 I don't do any exercise now, but I played hockey when I was young.

5 Meg doesn't like cooking although she cooks on special occasions.

6 Your uncle smokes rather a lot, doesn't he?

7 Have some more dessert; you've hardly eaten anything.

The use of *so* and *such*

The words *so* and *such* are often used as emphasizers, especially in spoken English. In the story, the people at the dinner party often speak in an exaggerated, emphatic way. Look at these examples from the story.

> '*Why is the middle class so stodgy – so utterly without a sense of humour!*'
>
> '*I have had such a dreadful experience with a taxi-man; he was most sinister.*'
>
> '*But you must not miss the last train. That's so awful, isn't it?*'

3 **What type of words follow *so* and *such*?**

4 **Rewrite these sentences using *so* or *such*. We have done the first one for you, as an example.**

1   I shall be very thankful not to have to travel alone.
    I shall be so very thankful not to have to travel alone.

2   The nurse had a very bad time trying to get the baby to sleep.

3   Eddie thought the play was wonderful.

4   The baby smiled at her in a very charming way.

5   'Thank-you for a marvellous party,' she said.

6   She looked different that night.

Adverbs of degree

Adverbs of degree can be used before adjectives, verbs or other adverbs to give information about the extent or amount of something. Bertha is overexcited and emphasizes most of her responses. Eddie Warren also frequently uses adverbs when expressing himself. Compare:

Bertha and Harry were good pals.   *Bertha and Harry were really good pals.*

It begins with a beautiful line.   *It begins with an incredibly beautiful line.*

5 **Look at these adverbs and answer the questions.**

incredibly   awfully   quite   really   utterly   dreadfully

a) Which adverb can mean: *not very* and *very much*?
b) Which adverb means *completely*?
c) Which adverbs can we use with gradable adjectives (*angry*, *hard*, *enjoyable* etc.)?

d) Which adverbs can we use with ungradable adjectives? (*terrible, awful, exhausted* etc.)?

6 Complete the following sentences with a suitable adverb.

1 By the time they arrived at his bedside, he was .... dead.
2 What an .... enchanting hat, my dear!
3 I saw a .... interesting film yesterday; I recommend it.
4 What an .... colourful painting!
5 I'm .... sorry that you weren't invited to the party.
6 She's a .... good musician, but she'll never be a professional.
7 He's an .... arrogant man; I couldn't vote for him.
8 I .... don't think that he will win the election.

Vocabulary used to portray character

Throughout the story, the narrative tells us about Bertha's feelings and thoughts. We see the other characters through her eyes.

7 Answer the questions.

1 Which people are these words associated with?
   a) *setting her lips … whispered … whispering … offended …*
   b) *rapped out the little voice … shouted … extravagantly cool and collected … zest for life … passion for fighting … a little ridiculous … saying abruptly … turned her violently … hideous grin*
   c) *silver … blonde … heavy eyelids … strange half-smile … pale fingers … moonbeam fingers … sleepy smile … slender*
2 Which word is also used to describe the pear tree?
3 What is the connection between the tree and the person described in c)?

The use of *must*

The word *must* is used frequently in the story. Look at these examples.

> '*Oh, I **must**!*' *said she.* [page 54]
>
> '*I **must** find out what that something is!*' [page 56]
>
> '*I **must** laugh or die.*' [page 62]

8 Now answer the questions.

1 What *must* Bertha do in each case?
2 What does the frequent use of *must* suggest about Bertha?

Literary analysis

Plot

1 What are the main events in the plot? Write a one-sentence summary of the plot.
2 What do you think is the most important event? How does the plot lead up to it? What happens as a consequence (result) of the event?
3 Which events come before the dinner party? What do we learn about Bertha's way of life?
4 Think about the scene where Bertha looks into the garden and sees the cats. Do you think she 'foresees' what is going to happen later?
5 What does the story tell us about relationships?

Character

6 What do you know about Bertha? Think about her age, her class, her status. Choose three adjectives to describe her.
7 Do you think Bertha is a privileged person? Why/Why not)?
8 Think about what you know about Harry from the story, his words and actions, and what Bertha thinks about him. What kind of person do you think he is – what is your impression of him?
9 What is your impression of Pearl? What words and phrases does Mansfield use to describe her?
10 Think about the Norman Knights and Eddie Warren. What is your impression of them? Would you enjoy going to a dinner party with them?
11 What do you think Bertha will do after the guests have gone? What do you think she *should* do?

Narration

12 The story is told in the third person but most events are 'filtered' through Bertha and her view of the world. Do you think the author shares Bertha's perspective? Does she agree with Bertha's opinions and attitudes?
13 Is it always clear when Bertha is thinking something and when she is saying it aloud? Find an example of this. What effect does it have?
14 What clues are there in the narrative that Bertha's life is not as perfect as she thinks, or tries to believe, it is? Look at the paragraph where Bertha thinks about her marriage.

15 What do you think the pear tree means to Bertha? Do you think the author intends it to be a symbol of something?

16 Look at pages 60–61 and the conversation at the dinner table. Is it always clear which character is speaking? What effect does this create? Why do you think Mansfield does this – what does it tell us about the conversation?

17 How would the story be different if written from Harry's, or Pearl's point of view?

Atmosphere

18 How does the author communicate Bertha's excitement at the beginning of the story?

19 How would you explain the atmosphere of the garden when Bertha first looks through the window? Think of the tree, the plants, the cats

20 What is your impression of the dinner party? Are people enjoying themselves? What do you think the author is trying to communicate?

21 Do you think the author prepares the reader for the final episode between Harry and Pearl, or is it a shock?

22 Which words and phrases are repeated throughout the story? Think about the pear tree, the moon, the description of Pearl Fulton. What effect does this create?

Style

23 Look at the first four paragraphs of the story.
    - How many sentences are there in the first two paragraphs?
    - Find examples of the following: interjection, exclamation, rhetorical question, quotation, direct speech.
    - What effect does this create?

24 Many of Bertha's thoughts are unclear and based on what she *thinks* rather than what she knows – her *intuition*. The author tells us about Bertha's *impressions* or *ideas* about the world, rather than concrete reality.

To convey this, Mansfield often uses the following phrases or words (highlighted in bold):

> **as though** you'd suddenly swallowed a bright piece of the afternoon sun
> **as if** they had said to each other: 'You too?'
> the dark table **seemed** to melt into the dusky light

Find some examples in the story. What do they describe?

25 The style of speaking of the middle-class characters – particularly the men – is often 'elliptical', that is, words are left out which are not essential to the meaning. For example, when Harry arrives home and runs up the stairs, he shouts *Hullo, you people. Down in five minutes.* (*I'll be* down in five minutes.') Can you find more examples of this?

26 At this period, it was fashionable in a certain group of people to use French words and phrases in conversation. Notice Bertha's use of *Entendu* when she speaks to Harry on the phone. Are there any other examples in the story?

27 The narrative changes frequently from Bertha's poetic view of life to the mundane – everyday, boring – reality and the guests' ridiculous comments. This emphasises to us how unrealistic Bertha is, and how much she is fooling herself.
Here is an example:

> 'For ever – for a moment? And did Miss Fulton murmur: 'Yes, just that.'
> Or did Bertha dream it?
> Then the light was snapped on and Face made the coffee…'

Find some more examples of this juxtaposition[56] – the immediate comparison – between Bertha's thoughts and the 'real' world.

28 Look at the passage beginning *While he looked it up she turned her head towards the hall.* [page 65]. How do you think Bertha feels? How does the author communicate the shock of her discovery?

Guidance to the above literary terms, answer keys to all the exercises and activities, plus a wealth of other reading-practice material, can be found on the student's section of the Macmillan Readers website at: www.macmillanenglish.com/readers.

---

56 placing or describing things together so that you can see how they are different

A Shocking Accident

by Graham Greene

About the author

Graham Greene was born in 1904 in Hertfordshire, England. As a boy, he attended Berkhamsted School where his father was headmaster. He later went to Oxford University where he published many poems and stories. In his early 20s he converted to Catholicism. Catholicism and inner conflict are important themes in books such as *The Power and the Glory* which is about a persecuted priest in Mexico.

Greene married when he was young and had two children. He separated from his wife in 1948 but they never divorced. He was reluctant to discuss his private life with journalists and it was only after he died that the public learned more about his personal life from his official biographer. He had many affairs, but his companion for many years until his death was Yvonne Cloetta.

Greene's first novel, *The Man Within*, was published in 1929. He was a prolific[1] writer. As well as novels, Greene also wrote travelogues such as *Journey Without Maps*, plays for stage and television, screenplays and short stories.

Throughout his life, Greene travelled widely and his books are set in a wide range of countries where his characters struggle with personal moral choices in turbulent[2] political settings. Greene admitted that he actively looked for adventure in areas of war and conflict.

Many of his books have been made into films, including *Brighton Rock*, *The Honorary Consul*, *The End of the Affair*, *The Quiet American* and *The Human Factor*. His most famous film is *The Third Man* for which he wrote the screenplay. Set in Vienna after the Second World War, it has many of the characteristics of Greene's writing: a background of conflict involving different countries, alienated characters, intrigue and preoccupation with moral choices.

Graham Greene was a friend of the British spy Kim Philby and some have suggested that Greene himself was a spy during his time in Africa where he worked for the British government. He sometimes

1 producing a lot of something
2 uncontrolled, suddenly and violently changing

joked about his Intelligence[3] activities, which he said were trivial[4]. This attitude can be seen in his book *Our Man in Havana*, in which the hero tries to sell a design for a vacuum cleaner as a deadly secret weapon.

Greene always refused to define himself politically. Although his books sometimes reflect anti-Americanism (*The Quiet American*), and he had some sympathy for left-wing regimes, he always denied having any definite political sympathies. Above all, he was a supporter of oppressed people everywhere and a clear-eyed observer of human behaviour in extreme situations.

In his later years, Greene lived in Antibes, in the south of France and continued to write prolifically. In 1990, he moved to Switzerland to be nearer to his daughter. He died in Vevey, Switzerland, in 1991, at the age of eighty-six.

About the story

A Shocking Accident was published in 1967 in the collection of stories *May We Borrow Your Husband?*. It was later made into a film which won an Oscar for Best Short Film in 1983.

Background information

The British education system

In the story, Jerome, the main character, attends a 'preparatory' or 'prep' school. This is an independent school for children aged between 7 or 8, and 11 or 13, and is often a boarding school where the pupils live.

In these schools, students are often divided into groups. Each group has its own teams and activities. The groups are called 'houses', and each one has its own master, a teacher who manages the students and events in the house. Jerome's housemaster is Mr Wordsworth.

In the second part of the story, Jerome is older and he attends a 'public school', which in the UK is, traditionally a single-sex boarding school, most of which were established in the 18th or 19th centuries.

---

3 information collected about the secret plans and activities of a foreign government, enemy etc
4 not very interesting, serious or valuable

Writers

Greene often wrote about his travels in some of the world's most remote and troubled places. In contrast, Jerome's father is a writer who seems to travel mainly in Mediterranean countries. His books are given unadventurous titles, such as *Sunshine and Shade*, *Rambles in the Balearics*, and *Nooks and Crannies* – suggesting, perhaps, that Jerome's father does not take risks. This makes the way he dies even more 'shocking'.

We learn that often, 'after an author's death', people write to the *Times Literary Supplement* expressing an interest in personal letters and stories about the writer's life. Greene tells us that most of these 'biographies' are never written and suggests that perhaps some of the more scandalous details are used as 'blackmail, that is – by threatening to reveal damaging information about someone. It is quite possible that Greene himself saw some examples of this type of behaviour.

Summary

It may help you to know something about what happens in the story before you read it. Don't worry, this summary does not tell you how the story ends!

Jerome, a young boy at a boarding school in England, is called one day to his housemaster's study. The housemaster tells him that his father, a travel writer, has died in Naples, Italy, as the result of a pig falling on him from a balcony.

As Jerome grows up, his father's death becomes a source of embarrassment to him. He mentally prepares different ways of telling the story in case anyone is interested in the future in writing his father's biography.

Jerome becomes engaged to Sally, a doctor's daughter. He realises that she will find out about his father's death when she meets his aunt, with whom he has been living. He tries to tell her himself, before the visit takes place, but all his attempts fail. A week before the wedding, Sally meets Jerome's aunt who tells her what happened to his father. Jerome is full of apprehension: what will Sally's reaction be?

Pre-reading exercises

Key vocabulary

This section will help you familiarise yourself with some of the more specific vocabulary used in the story. You may want to use it to help you before you start reading, or as a revision exercise after you have finished the story.

School vocabulary

housemaster a man who is a teacher and is in charge of a 'house' at a public school. A 'house' is one of the groups that students are divided into in some British schools, in order to compete against each other

headmaster a male teacher who is in charge of a school. Today, 'headteacher' is more common

preparatory school (prep school) in the UK, school for children between 7 or 8, and 11 or 13

public school in the UK, an independent boarding school for children between 11 or 13, and 18

break a period of time between lessons when students and teachers can rest, eat or play

trigonometry the part of mathematics that studies how the angles and sides of triangles are related

1 **Complete the following sentences with the words in the box above.**

1 When he was nine, Jerome attended a .... where, amongst other subjects, he studied ....

2 The owner of the school was also the .... and was not one of Jerome's teachers.

3 One day, during the .... between two lessons, Jerome was called into the study of his .... who informed him that his father had died.

4 It was not until Jerome was older and began to attend .... , that he began to find the manner of his father's death embarrassing.

Jerome's father

2 Look at the phrases in the box below, which refer to Jerome's father. Which do you think are 'objective' comments, made by the author? Which are made by Jerome's aunt or refer to Jerome's own feelings?

---

a) *a restless widowed author*

b) *a large sad man in an unsuitable dark suit posed in Capri*

c) *... my brother was a great traveller*

d) *Jerome's father had not been a very distinguished writer*

e) *He felt a longing to protect his memory, and uncertain whether this quiet love of his would survive ...*

f) *He wrote so tenderly about his travels. He would have had a great future.*

---

1 Which adjective tells you that Jerome's mother is dead?
2 Why do you think the suit is described as 'unsuitable'?
3 Which phrase tells us that Jerome's father was not a very well-known writer?
4 Which words suggest that Jerome's father was not content (happy)?
5 Which phrase do you think describes a photograph?

Main themes

Before you read the story, you may want to think about some of its main themes. The questions will help you think about the story as you're reading it for the first time. There is more discussion of the main themes in the *Literary analysis* section after the story.

Father-and-son relationships

It is interesting to see how Jerome's attitude to his father changes as he grows older. As a young boy, he idolises and romanticises him, imagining that he leads an exciting and dangerous life as an agent for the British Secret Service. He is sure that his death has been the result of a gun fight.

Later, at public school, he is teased by the other boys when they learn how Jerome's father died. By now, he knows his father was a travel writer rather than a secret agent. He accepts this, however, and cherishes the memory of his father and wants to keep it alive.

As a young man, he feels sympathy and *quiet love* for his father. It is essential to him that the girl he loves understands his feelings.

Reactions to death

Different cultures react to death in different ways. It is not rational that death from a falling pig should cause amusement. Nevertheless[5], in the story, most people who are not related to the person involved, find something comical in the event. Convention[6] tells us that we should receive news of a death with sympathy and seriousness but the housemaster, Jerome's schoolmates, and strangers, find it difficult to react in the conventional way. Because the cause of death is so unusual and unexpected, it makes people react in unusual and unexpected ways.

5 despite a fact or idea that you have just mentioned: used as a way of showing how a sentence, phrase, or word is related to what has already been said
6 a way of behaving that is generally accepted as being normal or right

A Shocking Accident

by Graham Greene

Jerome was called into his housemaster's room in the break between the second and the third class on a Thursday morning. He had no fear of trouble, for he was a warden – the name that the proprietor and headmaster of a rather expensive preparatory school had chosen to give to approved, reliable boys in the lower forms (from a warden one became a guardian and finally before leaving, it was hoped for Marlborough or Rugby[7], a crusader[8]). The housemaster, Mr Wordsworth, sat behind his desk with an appearance of perplexity[9] and **apprehension**. Jerome had the odd impression when he entered that he was a cause of fear.

'Sit down, Jerome,' Mr Wordsworth said. 'All going well with the trigonometry?'

'Yes, sir.'

'I've had a telephone call, Jerome. From your aunt. I'm afraid I have bad news for you.'

'Yes, sir?'

'Your father has had an accident.'

'Oh.'

Mr Wordsworth looked at him with some surprise. 'A serious accident.'

'Yes, sir?'

Jerome worshipped his father: the verb is exact. As man re-creates God, so Jerome re-created his father – from a restless widowed author into a mysterious adventurer who travelled in far places – Nice, Beirut, Majorca, even the Canaries. The time had arrived about his eighth birthday when Jerome believed

7 two prestigious independent schools, called 'public' schools in the UK
8 someone who works hard for a long time to achieve something that they believe is morally right
9 confused feeling because you cannot understand something; usually used as an adjective, *perplexed*

that his father either 'ran guns'[10] or was a member of the British Secret Service. Now it occurred to him that his father might have been wounded in a 'hail of machine-gun bullets'[11].

Mr Wordsworth played with the ruler on his desk. He seemed **at a loss** how to continue. He said, 'You know your father was in Naples?'

'Yes, sir.'

'Your aunt heard from the hospital today.'

'Oh.'

Mr Wordsworth said with desperation, 'It was a street accident.'

'Yes, sir?' It seemed quite likely to Jerome that they would call it a street accident. The police of course had fired first; his father would not take human life except **as a last resort**.

'I'm afraid your father was very seriously hurt indeed.'

'Oh.'

'In fact, Jerome, he died yesterday. Quite without pain.'

'Did they shoot him through the heart?'

'I beg your pardon. What did you say, Jerome?'

'Did they shoot him through the heart?'

'Nobody shot him, Jerome. A pig fell on him.' An inexplicable[12] **convulsion** took place in the nerves of Mr Wordsworth's face; it really looked for a moment as though he were going to laugh. He closed his eyes, composed his features and said rapidly as though it were necessary to **expel** the story as rapidly as possible. 'Your father was walking along a street in Naples when a pig fell on him. A shocking accident. Apparently in the poorer quarters of Naples they keep pigs on their balconies. This one was on the fifth floor. It had grown too fat. The balcony broke. The pig fell on your father.'

Mr Wordsworth left his desk rapidly and went to the window, turning his back on Jerome. He shook a little with emotion.

Jerome said, 'What happened to the pig?'

10 *gun running* is taking guns into a country secretly and illegally
11 a large number of bullets that come at you quickly and with force
12 impossible to explain

This was not **callousness** on the part of Jerome, as it was interpreted by Mr Wordsworth to his colleagues (he even discussed with them whether, perhaps, Jerome was yet fitted[13] to be a warden). Jerome was only attempting to visualize the strange scene to get the details right. Nor was Jerome a boy who cried; he was a boy who **brooded**, and it never occurred to him at his preparatory school that the circumstances of his father's death were comic – they were still part of the mystery of life. It was later, in his first term at his public school, when he told the story to his best friend, that he began to realize how it affected others. Naturally after that disclosure he was known, rather unreasonably, as Pig.

Unfortunately his aunt had no sense of humour. There was an enlarged snapshot[14] of his father on the piano; a large sad man in an unsuitable dark suit posed in Capri with an umbrella (to guard him against sunstroke), the Faraglione rocks forming the background. By the age of sixteen Jerome was well aware that the portrait looked more like the author of *Sunshine and Shade* and *Rambles in the Balearics* than an agent of the Secret Service. All the same he loved the memory of his father: he still possessed an album fitted with picture-postcards (the stamps had been soaked off long ago for his other collection), and it pained him when his aunt embarked[15] with strangers on the story of his father's death.

'A shocking accident,' she would begin, and the stranger would compose his or her features into the correct shape for interest and **commiseration**. Both reactions, of course, were false, but it was terrible for Jerome to see how suddenly, midway in her **rambling discourse**, the interest would become genuine. 'I can't think how such things can be allowed in a **civilized** country,' his aunt would say. 'I suppose one has to regard Italy as civilized. One is prepared for all kinds of things abroad, of course, and my brother was a great traveller. He always carried a

---

13 right, suitable (in modern English, we usually say *to be fit to do/be something*)
14 a photograph taken without the use of professional equipment
15 to start on a new project or activity; here, to begin to tell the story of his father's death

water-filter with him. It was far less expensive, you know, than buying all those bottles of mineral water. My brother always said that his filter paid for his dinner wine. You can see from that what a careful man he was, but who could possibly have expected when he was walking along the Via Dottore Manuele Panucci on his way to the Hydrographic Museum[16] that a pig would fall on him?' That was the moment when the interest became genuine.

Jerome's father had not been a very **distinguished** writer, but the time always seems to come, after an author's death, when somebody thinks it worth his while to write a letter to the *Times Literary Supplement*[17] announcing the preparation of a biography and asking to see any letters or documents or receive any **anecdotes** from friends of the dead man. Most of the biographies, of course, never appear – one wonders whether the whole thing may not be an obscure form of **blackmail** and whether many a potential writer of a biography or thesis finds the means in this way to finish his education at Kansas or Nottingham[18]. Jerome, however, as a chartered accountant[19], lived far from the literary world. He did not realize how small the menace[20] really was, or that the danger period for someone of his father's **obscurity** had long passed. Sometimes he rehearsed the method of recounting his father's death so as to reduce the comic element to its smallest dimensions – it would be of no use to refuse information, for in that case the biographer would undoubtedly visit his aunt who was living to a great old age with no sign of **flagging**.

It seemed to Jerome that there were two possible methods – the first led gently up to the accident, so that by the time it was described the listener was so well prepared that the death came really as an anti-climax. The chief danger of laughter in such a story was surprise. When he rehearsed this method Jerome began boringly enough.

16 *hydrographic* refers to the science of the study of water
17 *The Times* is a British newspaper and *The Times Literary Supplement* publishes book reviews and articles about authors
18 refer to the universities of Kansas (USA) and Nottingham (UK)
19 an accountant is someone whose job is to prepare financial records for a company or person; *chartered* means that they have passed a professional examination
20 someone or something that is dangerous and likely to cause you harm

'You know Naples and those high tenement[21] buildings? Someone once told me that the Neapolitan always feels at home in New York just as the man from Turin feels at home in London because the river runs in much the same way in both cities. Where was I? Oh, yes. Naples, of course. You'd be surprised in the poorer quarters[22] what things they keep on the balconies of those sky-scraping tenements – not washing, you know, or bedding, but things like livestock, chickens or even pigs. Of course the pigs get no exercise whatever and fatten all the quicker.' He could imagine how his hearer's eyes would have **glazed** by this time. 'I've no idea, have you, how heavy a pig can be, but these old buildings are all badly in need of repair. A balcony on the fifth floor gave way under one of those pigs. It struck the third floor balcony on its way down and sort of **ricocheted** into the street. My father was on the way to the Hydrographic Museum when the pig hit him. Coming from that height and that angle it broke his neck.' This was really a **masterly** attempt to make an **intrinsically** interesting subject boring.

The other method Jerome rehearsed had the virtue of brevity.

'My father was killed by a pig.'

'Really? In India?'

'No, in Italy.'

'How interesting. I never realized there was pig-sticking[23] in Italy. Was your father keen on polo[24]?'

In course of time, neither too early nor too late, rather as though, in his capacity as a chartered accountant, Jerome had studied the statistics and taken the average, he became engaged to be married: to a pleasant fresh-faced girl of twenty-five whose father was a doctor in Pinner. Her name was Sally, her favourite author was still Hugh Walpole[25], and she had adored babies ever since she had been given a doll at the age of five which moved its eyes and made water. Their relationship was contented

21 *unusual, old-fashioned*: a large building in a city, containing several flats/apartments
22 part or area of a town or city
23 to chase and kill pigs with a sharply pointed stick
24 a game played on horseback with a long pole and a ball
25 a popular, early 20th-century novelist who wrote family sagas

rather than exciting, as **became** the love-affair of a chartered accountant; it would never have done if it had interfered with the figures.

One thought worried Jerome, however. Now that within a year he might himself become a father, his love for the dead man increased; he realized what affection had gone into the picture-postcards. He felt a longing to protect his memory, and uncertain whether this quiet love of his would survive if Sally were so insensitive as to laugh when she heard the story of his father's death. Inevitably she would hear it when Jerome brought her to dinner with his aunt. Several times he tried to tell her himself, as she was naturally anxious to know all she could that concerned him.

'You were very small when your father died?'

'Just nine.'

'Poor little boy,' she said.

'I was at school. They broke the news to me.'

'Did you take it very hard?'

'I can't remember.'

'You never told me how it happened.'

'It was very sudden. A street accident.'

'You'll never drive fast, will you, Jemmy?' (She had begun to call him 'Jemmy'.) It was too late then to try the second method – the one he thought of as the pig-sticking one.

They were going to marry quietly in a registry-office[26] and have their honeymoon[27] at Torquay. He avoided taking her to see his aunt until a week before the wedding, but then the night came, and he could not have told himself whether his apprehension was more for his father's memory or the security of his own love.

The moment came all too soon. 'Is that Jemmy's father?' Sally asked, picking up the portrait of the man with the umbrella.

'Yes, dear. How did you guess?'

'He has Jemmy's eyes and brow, hasn't he?'

'Has Jerome lent you his books?'

26 a place where you can get married without a religious ceremony
27 a holiday that two people take after they get married

'No.'

'I will give you a set for your wedding. He wrote so tenderly about his travels. My own favourite is *Nooks and Crannies*[28]. He would have had a great future. It made that shocking accident all the worse.'

'Yes?'

Jerome longed[29] to leave the room and not see that loved face crinkle with irresistible amusement.

'I had so many letters from his readers after the pig fell on him.' She had never been so **abrupt** before.

And then the miracle happened. Sally did not laugh. Sally sat with open eyes of horror while his aunt told her the story, and at the end, 'How horrible,' Sally said. 'It makes you think, doesn't it? Happening like that. Out of a clear sky.'

Jerome's heart sang with joy. It was as though she had **appeased** his fear for ever. In the taxi going home he kissed her with more passion than he had ever shown and she returned it. There were babies in her pale blue pupils, babies that rolled their eyes and made water.

'A week today,' Jerome said, and she squeezed his hand. 'Penny for your thoughts[30], my darling.'

'I was wondering,' Sally said, 'what happened to the poor pig?'

'They almost certainly had it for dinner,' Jerome said happily and kissed the dear child again.

28 every part of a place
29 wanted very much
30 *spoken*: used for asking someone what they are thinking about

Post-reading exercises

Understanding the story

1 Use these questions to help you check that you have understood the story.

Part 1

1 Is Jerome afraid when he is called into the housemaster's room? Why/why not?
2 Who has telephoned the school? Why?
3 What are Jerome's feelings for his father? What does he think his father does?
4 How does Jerome imagine that his father has died?
5 How does Mr Wordsworth react when he tells Jerome how his father died? Greene writes that the housemaster *shook with emotion*. What kind of emotion do you think Wordsworth is feeling?

Part 2

6 Does Jerome show a lot of emotion when he hears about his father's death?
7 When does Jerome realise that other people find his father's death comical?
8 Why has Jerome got so many postcards? Does he remember his father with love?
9 Why is it *terrible* for Jerome to listen to his aunt telling other people about his father's death?
10 Is it likely that anyone in the literary world will ask Jerome for details about his father's life? Why/why not?
11 Is Jerome aware of his father's position in the literary world?
12 How many explanations of his father's death has Jerome prepared for other people? Are the explanations very different?
13 How would you describe the relationship between Jerome and Sally?
14 What is Jerome afraid of with regard to[31] Sally and his father?
15 Why does Jerome long to leave the room when Sally is talking to his aunt?
16 What is the *miracle* and why does Jerome's heart sing with joy?
17 Does the story have a happy ending?

---

31 *phrase 'with regard to'*: concerning/about/relating to

Language study

Grammar

The use of *one*

The use of the indefinite personal pronoun *one* is used to talk about people in general, including the speaker. It is quite formal and often creates distance. If used a lot it can make the speaker sound pompous[32]. The more informal pronoun *you* can usually be used instead.

1 Look at the examples from the text, in the box below.

> a) ... *from a warden one became a guardian* ...
> b) *I suppose one has to regard Italy as civilized* ...
> c) *One is prepared for all kinds of things abroad, of course* ...
> d) ... *one wonders whether the whole thing may not be an obscure form of blackmail* ...

1 Which sentences are spoken by Jerome's aunt?
2 Who does *one* refer to in the first sentence?
3 Who *wonders* in the last sentence?

2 Rewrite these sentences in a more formal way, using the pronoun *one*. We have done the first one for you, as an example.

1 You never know when something terrible might happen to you.
One never knows when something terrible might happen to one.

2 You should never have your suits made by amateurs.

3 You should always give yourself plenty of time to get to the airport.

4 I don't think you should ever drink wine with your oysters.

5 If you want to see wonderful buildings you must go to Italy.

6 Your opinions are only important if they coincide with his.

---

32 someone who is pompous thinks they are very important and speaks or behaves in a very serious and formal way

The use of the passive

3 **Greene often uses the passive voice which makes the text sound more formal. Look at these examples from the text in the box below, and consider the following questions:**

a) How is the passive used in each sentence?

b) What effect does this have?

> ... *from a warden one became a guardian and finally before leaving, it was hoped for Marlborough or Rugby, a crusader.*
> *Naturally, after that disclosure he was known, rather unreasonably, as Pig.*
> ... *she had adored babies ever since she had been given a doll at the age of five which moved its eyes and made water.*

4 **Rewrite the following sentences using the passive voice. We have done the first one for you, as an example.**

1 The housemaster called Jerome into his office.
Jerome was called into the housemaster's office.

2 He learned that a pig had struck his father and killed him.

3 He removed the stamps from the postcards and made them into a collection.

4 Some people thought the story of Jerome's father's death rather amusing.

5 Jerome's career did not upset his marriage plans in any way.

6 The author hopes that Sally and Jerome will live happily ever after.

Vocabulary to create comic effect

Greene achieves a comic effect by using formal, sometimes pompous language, which contrasts with the events or circumstances being described. Consider the language used by Jerome's aunt when she is talking about Italy and other countries. She uses *one* to refer to herself, creating a distance between herself and Italy, very formally asserting that she and the British are – of course –*civilized* – this is without question. However, all other countries are potentially *uncivilized*:

I can't think how such things can be allowed in a civilized country,' his aunt would say. 'I suppose one has to regard Italy as civilized. One is prepared for all kinds of things abroad, of course ...

The comedy arises from the fact that she is clearly making unreasonable generalisations about Italy and other countries, whilst it is not clear whether she has actually travelled 'abroad' at all.

5 **Rewrite the following sentences from the story in a simpler, less formal way.**

1 *An inexplicable convulsion took place in the nerves of Mr. Wordsworth's face.*

2 *...it pained him when his aunt embarked with strangers on the story of his father's death.*

3 *Sometimes he rehearsed the method of recounting his father's death so as to reduce the comic element to its smallest dimensions.*

Literary analysis

Plot

1 What is the *shocking accident* in the story? How do most people feel when they hear about it? How do you think *you* would react?
2 How old is Jerome when his father dies? Do you think this affects Jerome's reactions?
3 How old is Jerome when the story finishes? How has the manner of his father's death affected him during his life?
4 How many accounts are there in the story of Jerome's father's death? Think about Mr Wordsworth, Jerome, and his aunt.
5 How are the accounts of the death different? Who finds it difficult to tell the story? Who finds it easier? Why?
6 How do you think Jerome would have felt if Sally had laughed at his aunt's story? Would the story have ended differently?
7 This story was made into a short film. What changes do you think were made? Think about characters, setting and plot.

Character

8   How would you describe Jerome's father? How does he change in Jerome's eyes as the boy grows older?

9   What kind of person is Jerome? Do you think he is like his father?

10 How would you describe Jerome's aunt? What does she think of her brother? Give evidence for your answer.

11 What kind of person is Sally? Do you think she and Jerome are suited to each other?

12 Do you think the type of schooling that Jerome receives affects his character or attitudes? How?

Narration

13 What do you think Greene's attitude is to his characters? Do you think he identifies with some characters more than others? If so, which?

14 Do you think Greene is a sympathetic narrator or a cynical observer of human nature?

15 Why do you think Greene makes Jerome a chartered accountant and Sally a doctor's daughter who *adored babies*? How do these details contrast with the main event at the centre of the story?

16 Do you think Greene succeeds in making us feel sympathy towards Jerome? How?

Atmosphere

17 How would you describe the atmosphere of the story? Are any of the following adjectives appropriate?

amusing   bizarre   absurd   sad   cynical   well-observed
true-to-life   unrealistic

Can you think of any more adjectives?

18 Are people's reactions to the pig incident understandable? Why/why not?

19 Is the story believable or is it exaggerated? Explain your answer.

Style

20 Look again at the first paragraph of the story [page 81] and the beginning of the conversation between Mr Wordsworth and Jerome. Notice how Greene obtains a comic effect by using both long, formal sentences and short, spoken sentences. Find more examples of this kind of narrative in the story.

21 Look at the aunt's question [page 84] ending '... *but who could possibly have expected when he was walking along the Via Dottore Manuele Panucci on his way to the Hydrographic Museum that a pig would fall on him?*' What effect do the details of the place have? Can you find other places where unnecessary detail is given? What effect does it have?

22 Wordsworth's question, '*All going well with the trigonometry?*' [page 81] is absurd in the circumstances – so inappropriate that it is funny. It shows how difficult Mr Wordsworth finds it to tell Jerome of his father's death, and how uncomfortable he is in this situation. What other questions are there which create a comic effect?

23 Culturally, the English are known for their use of understatement. For example, they might say 'It was rather cold' when they really mean 'It was absolutely freezing!' Greene is very 'English' in this respect. Look at these examples of understatement from the story.
Naturally, after that disclosure he was known, rather unreasonably, as Pig. (It was a very unreasonable and cruel nickname.)
Jerome's father had not been a very distinguished writer. (He had been a bad writer.)
Can you find any more examples of understatement in the story?

24 Greene often uses irony in his writing – a form of humour where the literal meaning is the opposite of the actual meaning, it can sound as though you are being serious, but actually you are being sarcastic. Notice below, how he describes Jerome's profession and how it affects his relationship with Sally.

In course of time, neither too early nor too late, rather as though, in his capacity as a chartered accountant, Jerome had studied the statistics and taken the average, he became engaged to be married.

Their relationship was contented rather than exciting, as became the love affair of a chartered accountant; it would never have done if it had interfered with the figures.

What does the description suggest about Jerome's attitude to love and marriage? What is Greene suggesting about the profession of chartered accountancy and the people who do this job? Could you rewrite this paragraph in a sentence, to expose what Greene is *actually* saying about Jerome? Do you agree with Greene's comments? What other professions tend to be associated with certain characteristics?

Look again at the paragraph [page 81] beginning 'Jerome worshipped his father...' Can you find another example of Greene's irony?

Guidance to the above literary terms, answer keys to all the exercises and activities, plus a wealth of other reading-practice material, can be found on the student's section of the Macmillan Readers website at: www.macmillanenglish.com/readers.

The Jilting of Jane
by H G Wells

About the author

Herbert George Wells is best known today for his 'scientific romances', a genre that we now call 'science fiction'. Books such as *The Time Machine* (1895), *The Island of Dr Moreau* (1896), *The War of the Worlds* (1898) and *The First Men on the Moon* (1901) are considered to be classics of the genre[1] and have often been dramatised for radio, TV and the cinema. In one famous episode, in 1938, the US film director and actor Orson Welles announced on the radio that the world was about to be invaded by aliens. He based his report on *The War of the Worlds*, and it was so realistic that it caused panic among US citizens. Orson had intended it as a joke, but later had to apologise to the public and to Wells himself.

Herbert George Wells was born in 1866 in Bromley, Kent in the south of England. He was one of four children. His parents had a shop and his father was a professional cricketer until he broke his leg. The shop was not very successful, money was short, and Wells was sent to a cheap and badly-run[2] private school. Wells educated himself mostly, and he read widely from the books in the library of Uppark, the large country house where his mother worked, first as a lady's maid and later as housekeeper[3].

Aged 14, when his father's business failed, Wells worked as an **apprentice**[4] to a draper[5]. He described his two years there as 'the most unhappy, hopeless period of my life.' He recorded this period in his book *Kipps* (1905), a vivid[6] account of the lives of workers in the retail trade.

1 a particular style used in cinema, writing or art, which can be recognised by certain features
2 not well-managed or organised
3 someone whose job it is to clean someone else's house, and sometimes cook their meals
4 someone who works for a particular person or company, usually for low pay, to learn the type of work they do
5 someone who sells cloth and things made of cloth
6 clear and detailed

In 1883, Wells became a student and teacher at Midhurst Grammar School. He then obtained a scholarship to the Normal School of Science in London where he studied a range of subjects, including biology. However, he lost interest in his studies, and he left without a degree, in 1887. Wells taught in private schools for four years and in 1890 he finally gained a first-class degree in zoology. In the early 1890s, he became a freelance[7] journalist and then began to write fiction. Despite his success as a writer of fiction, Wells always said that he was, above all, a journalist, with an interest in facts and the development of society.

In 1891, Wells settled in London and married his cousin, Isabel. The marriage was not a success. Wells left Isabel for one of his adult students, Amy Catherine Robbins, whom he married in 1895. Wells had many affairs with other women but Amy remained a supportive wife until her death in 1927.

Wells's first novel was *The Time Machine*, about a man who travels into the future and returns with incredible stories. Much of the atmosphere is achieved by carefully-studied technical details. The book is also a parody[8] of English class division. Wells was very interested in politics. He was a member of the Fabian Society, which was founded in 1884. Its members were mostly left-wing, middle-class intellectuals who agreed with socialist ideas but rejected violent revolution[9] and Communism. In 1905, Wells published *A Modern Utopia* in which he describes a world run by a group of wise men who eliminate 'useless' people. In the early 1920s, Wells was a candidate for parliament for the Labour party, but failed to win a seat.

Between 1924 and 1933, Wells lived mostly in France. In 1934, he had meetings with both Stalin, who left him disappointed, and Roosevelt. He tried without success to recruit them to his world-saving schemes.

Wells returned to London and lived there during World War II. His last book, *Mind at the End of its Tether* (1945) was not hopeful about man's future. He died in London in 1946. During his life he wrote nearly 50 novels, many short stories, and numerous articles and works of non-fiction.

7 not permanently employed by one company but sells their services to more than one company
8 a literary or musical work that copies a serious work in a humorous way
9 the overthrow of a government or political system, usually by force, replacing it with another system

About the story

The Jilting[10] of Jane was first published in 1894 in the *Pall Mall Gazette*, an evening newspaper. In 1911, it was included in a collection of Wells's short stories, *The Country of the Blind and Other Stories*.

Background information

The draper's shop

Drapers' shops were very common at the time this story was written. They sold mostly cloth or things made of cloth, for people's homes. A lot of the customers were middle-class women who thought that it was very important that the people who served in the shop were polite and *gentlemanly*.

In the story, William is second porter[11] at a draper's shop and is then promoted to head porter. He begins to serve customers in the shop; his next promotion will make him an *assistant*. Wells, like his brothers, had worked in a draper's shop himself and experienced its boring routine when he was an apprentice. In his second year in the job, a new apprentice was employed who did some of the more boring jobs. Unfortunately, he also took on some of the tasks that had enabled Wells to escape occasionally from the shop.

Religion

At this time, the Church of England was the official Christian Church in England, as it is today. The reigning king or queen is its leader. Some of the Anglican priests (or *ministers*) had the title of Reverend. They sometimes held outdoor services for the workers after the official church services. In the story, the Reverend Barnabus Baux holds services on the street corner after evensong[12] on Sundays. This informal outdoor service seems to involve mostly hymn-singing and provides the young people with an opportunity to meet up and flirt with each other.

William's father is *Church* (of England) but William himself goes to chapel (a smaller church) and belongs to the Plymouth Brethren[13],

10 *old-fashioned, formal:* to tell someone that you want to end your romantic relationship with them
11 someone in a station, airport, or hotel whose job is helping people with their bags and showing them where to go
12 the church service in the Anglican Church that people go to in the evening
13 *old-fashioned, religious:* an old word meaning *brothers*. Here, it refers to the male members of a religious group, the Plymouth Brethren

one of the nonconformist religions that grew up in the 18th century. These religions belonged to the Protestant Christian tradition but their churches and services were simpler than those of the Anglican Church.

Self-help books

One of the most widely-sold books in the 19th century was *Mrs Beeton's Book of Household Management* (1861). It gives advice to housewives on cooking, etiquette[14], entertaining and managing your servants.

In the story, Euphemia looks up the etiquette for Jane concerning wearing her engagement[15] ring when serving dinner, in *Enquire Within* and *Mrs Motherly's Book of Household Management*. These titles were probably invented, but refer to the kind of books that were popular at the time.

William also consults a book which has been given to him by his manager. Jane describes it as *Smiles 'Elp* (help) *Yourself* and explains that it tells you how to *get on in the world*, or be successful. This shows that self-help books were as popular at the time as they are today.

Summary

It may help you to know something about what happens in the story before you read it. Don't worry, this summary does not tell you how the story ends!

The narrator of the story is a respectable middle-class man living in London with his wife Euphemia. They have several servants. Jane is one of their servants, and she has changed from a person who never stopped talking and singing, into a much quieter and more serious girl.

The reason for this change, is the fact that Jane has been jilted by her young man, William, to whom she has been engaged to be married for three years.

Most of what the narrator knows about William has come from his wife, who is friendly towards the servants. William is second porter at Maynard's, the drapers; after the head porter leaves, he is promoted and given more money. Soon, William is dressing more

14 *old-fashioned, formal:* a set of rules for behaving correctly in social situations
15 formal agreement between two people to be married, shown by the woman wearing a ring

smartly. Jane tells Euphemia that William is *a lot above* her. She reports that William is going to serve customers in the shop, and that if he does it well, he will become an assistant.

One Sunday, William does not come to the house to take Jane out, as he usually does. Jane asks permission to go out on the following two Sundays. She admits that William is going out with another girl, a milliner[16], who also plays the piano. Jane has followed them and told the girl that she is engaged to William. The couple have ignored Jane.

On August Bank Holiday, William, his new girlfriend and the girl's mother visit a museum in South Kensington. Jane stops them in the street and claims her right to William. The three people threaten to have Jane arrested by the police, then escape the situation in a cab[17]. Euphemia tells Jane that William does not deserve her, and that he is not good enough for her. Jane admits that he is weak but blames his new girlfriend for taking him from her.

One day, Jane asks for permission to go to William's wedding. She takes with her some boots and shoes in a bag. When she comes back, she describes the wedding and admits that she threw a boot at the bride[18], which in fact, hit William. She believes that she gave him a black eye[19].

Pre-reading exercises

Key vocabulary

This section will help you familiarise yourself with some of the more specific vocabulary used in the story. You may want to use it to help you before you start reading, or as a revision exercise after you have finished the story.

Formal words and expressions

The narrator is a comfortably-off (quite wealthy), middle-class person. His words suggest he is well educated, and he views the events in his household from a distance and with ironic humour. He uses formal

16 *old-fashioned*: someone whose job is to make or sell hats
17 taxi
18 a woman who is getting married
19 a bruise on the skin around the eye as a result of being hit

words and expressions which emphasise his character. At times he can sound rather pompous. Many of the words that he uses are now also old-fashioned.

1 **The list below gives meanings for some of the more unusual words, which will help you to follow the story.**

accost to stop someone and speak to them, especially in a way that could make them feel embarrassed or annoyed

aggrieved feeling angry or unhappy because you think you have been treated in an unfair way

cardinal very important

discourse on to talk for a long time about a particular subject

fervour very strong feeling or enthusiasm

inalienable this refers to something which cannot be taken away from you or given to someone else

latterly recently

partake to be involved in an activity, share

reprehensible very bad and deserving to be criticised

singularly in a noticeable way, particularly

thus in this way

to be wont to do sthg to have a habit of doing something

to extort confidences to get private information from someone by using force or threats

with promptitude quickly, immediately

Informal words and expressions

In contrast to the formal language described above, there a number of informal or colloquial phrases in the story. These are nearly always used by Jane, in her conversations with Euphemia.

2 **Look at these examples from the story. Can you guess what they mean?**

'I believe Jane **keeps him in ties**.'

'He is **getting on**, Jane,' said my wife.

'William is **being led away**,' she remarked abruptly.

We do not know the details ... but only such fragments as poor Jane **let fall**.

She did, I think, go so far as **to lay hands on him**.

'I only threw that one. I **hadn't the heart** to try again.'

'It **serves me right**. I was stuck up about him.'

3 Match the phrases with their definitions.

1 to keep someone in something	a) to think you are better than you are
2 to get on	b) to attack someone physically
3 to be led away	c) to pay for someone to buy something
4 to let (something) fall	d) not to feel like doing something
5 to lay hands on someone	e) to make progress
6 (not) to have the heart do something	f) to make someone behave badly
7 to be stuck up	g) to deserve something
8 to serve someone right	h) to give someone information

Spoken language

The way the author writes dialogue shows the class divisions which existed at the time. The conversations between the narrator and his wife are written in standard English. Jane's speech shows her own social status as a servant. The author uses non-standard spelling to represent her Cockney[20] accent and pronunciation.

Accent and pronunciation

4 Here are some of the things Jane says in the story. Look at the words in bold. Match them to the standard English words in the box below.

carriage madam gave bankrupt amethyst greengrocer an angel tumor aren't

1 *His father was a **greengrosher**, **m'm**, and had a **chumor**, and he was **bankrup'** twice.*
2 *...he is saving money to buy a ring – **hammyfist**.*
3 *I'm sure the master's **a hangel** when his pipe's alight.*
4 *Mr Maynard comes and talks to him quite friendly, when they **ain't** busy...*
5 *It was a real **kerridge** they had, not a fly.*
6 ***Gev** him a black eye, I should think*

---

20 the accent and dialect of English spoken by people from the East End of London

Non-standard English

5 Here are some of the non-standard features that we can see in Jane's speech. Look at these examples and rewrite them in standard English. We have done the first one for you, as an example.

1 *Yes, m'm; and he don't smoke.*
'Yes, madam, and he doesn't smoke.'

2 *Smoking ... do make such a dust about.*

3 *It tells you how to get on in the world, and some what William read to me was lovely, ma'am.*

4 *Mr Maynard has took a great fancy to him.*

5 *It could not have been a very agreeable walk, Jane.*
Not for no parties, ma'am.

Main themes

Before you read the story, you may want to think about some of its main themes. The questions will help you think about the story as you are reading it for the first time. There is more discussion of the main themes in the *Literary analysis* section after the story.

Respectability, class and social climbing

It is interesting to see what Jane thinks makes William respectable. She boasts that he does not drink alcohol or smoke. He goes to church and is a member of the Plymouth Brethren, a Christian group that did not follow all the traditions of the Anglican Church. He reads the self-help book that Mr Maynard gives him with great interest and is determined to *get on* – to make progress in his job. He tries hard to improve his way of speaking, as this is important when serving customers. He is promoted to head porter and then is given the chance to serve in the shop. Each time his wage goes up, William becomes more ambitious. The improvements in his condition are reflected in his new clothes and the fact that he leaves Jane, a servant, for a milliner who plays the piano, something that Jane wishes she could do, as it is a sign of greater education and culture.

6 As you read the story, ask yourself:

a) Why does Jane think William will be a *good match* for her?

b) Do you feel sorry for Jane? Why/why not?

H G Wells was very interested in class, and the ways it operated in society, valuing some people more than others. In this story, as in many others, he shows how social-climbing – trying to be wealthier, more respectable, more *accomplished* (having artistic skills such as playing the piano) and therefore more valued – touches everyone's lives and opinions. Wells shows that characters on all *rungs of the social ladder* judge each other on the basis of social, and class, rules and conventions. The narrator, for example, describes his wife's friendliness with the servants as *reprehensible*. But the servants also think some people are better than others, on the basis of jobs and money, as we can see from the following extract. Jane describes William to Euphemia:

> *His relatives are quite superior people, m'm. Not labouring people at all.*

This is a good example of Wells's sense of irony – after all, Jane herself is a kind of 'labourer', working as a servant. She uses the word *papa* to refer to William's father, in an awkward attempt to use language usually used by upper-class people – Euphemia has to ask her to repeat herself:

> *'He goes to chapel,' said Jane. 'His papa[21], ma'am–'*
> *'His what, Jane?'*
> *'His papa, ma'am'...*

Wells even says that Euphemia *'didn't fancy him [William] much'* but took an interest in him because of signs of his respectability, such as his llama-skin umbrella. Jane herself is a social climber and a snob, looking down on others. She recognises this herself later in the story:

> *It serves me right. I was stuck up about him.*

She can see that she considered herself better than other people because she was engaged to William.

7 As you read the story, look for other examples of class division and snobbery.

21 *old-fashioned:* a word meaning *father*, used in the past, particularly by the upper classes

Courtship / the conventions of romantic relationships

Jane is free to go out and meet young men, but she must follow certain rules when she meets William. The *mistress of the house*, her employer, Euphemia, asks if the young couple are engaged and Jane says that William is saving his money to buy a ring. Euphemia says that once they are *properly engaged* William may come and have tea in the kitchen on Sunday afternoons. Sunday is Jane's day off when she can *walk out* with William. She puts on her best clothes and one day she is wearing new, cotton gloves.

When William leaves Jane, she is furious[22] and confronts him. When William is finally married, Jane goes against convention and waits outside the church for the married couple to appear. She then throws a boot at the bride, but hits William instead.

8 As you read the story, ask yourself:

a) Was Jane aiming too high, socially, in wanting to marry William?

b) Do you admire her for fighting in the street and throwing the boot?

22 extremely angry

The Jilting of Jane

by H G Wells

As I sit writing in my study, I can hear our Jane bumping her way downstairs with a brush and **dustpan**. She used in the old days to sing hymn tunes, or the British national song for the time being, to these instruments, but latterly she has been silent and even careful over her work. Time was[23] when I prayed with fervour[24] for such silence, and my wife with sighs for such care, but now they have come we are not so glad as we might have **anticipated** we should be. Indeed, I would rejoice[25] secretly, though it may be unmanly weakness to admit it, even to hear Jane sing 'Daisy'[26] or, by the fracture[27] of any plate but[28] one of Euphemia's best green ones, to learn that the period of brooding has come to an end.

Yet how we longed to hear the last of Jane's young man before we heard the last of him! Jane was always very free with her conversation to my wife, and discoursed admirably in the kitchen on a variety of topics – so well, indeed, that I sometimes left my study door open – our house is a small one – to partake of it. But after William came, it was always William, nothing but William; William this and William that; and when we thought William was worked out and exhausted altogether, then William all over again. The engagement lasted altogether three years; yet how she got introduced to William, and so became thus **saturated** with him, was always a secret. For my part, I believe it was at the street corner where the Rev. Barnabas Baux used to hold an

23 *old-fashioned, dialect:* in the past
24 *formal, literary, old-fashioned:* very strong feeling or emotion
25 *mostly religious:* to feel very happy about something, or to celebrate something in a happy way
26 a popular song at the time the story was written
27 *formal, medical:* break
28 *literary, old-fashioned:* except for

open-air service after evensong on Sundays. Young Cupids[29] were wont to **flit** like **moths** round the paraffin flare of that centre of High Church[30] hymn-singing. I fancy[31] she stood singing hymns there, out of memory and her imagination, instead of coming home to get supper, and William came up beside her and said, 'Hello!' 'Hello yourself!' she said; and **etiquette** being satisfied, they proceeded to converse.

As Euphemia has a reprehensible way of letting her servants talk to her, she soon heard of him. 'He is *such* a respectable young man, ma'am,' said Jane, 'you don't know'. Ignoring the slur[32] cast on her acquaintance, my wife inquired further about this William.

'He is second **porter** at Maynard's, the draper's,' said Jane, 'and gets eighteen shillings[33] – nearly a pound – a week, m'm; and when the head porter leaves he will be head porter. His relatives are quite superior people, m'm. Not labouring people at all. His father was a green-grosher, m'm, and had a chumor, and he was bankrup' twice. And one of his sisters is in a Home for the Dying. It will be a very good match for me, m'm,' said Jane, 'me being an **orphan** girl.'

'Then you are engaged to him?' asked my wife.

'Not engaged, ma'am; but he is saving money to buy a ring – hammyfist.'

'Well, Jane, when you are properly engaged to him you may ask him round here on Sunday afternoons, and have tea with him in the kitchen'; for my Euphemia has a motherly conception of her duty towards her maid-servants. And presently the amethystine[34] ring was being worn about the house, even with ostentation[35],

29 Cupid was the Roman god of love, commonly depicted as a baby boy with wings, carrying a bow and arrow, aiming for people's hearts, to make them fall in love
30 the part of the Anglican Church that emphasises tradition and church authority
31 *literary, old-fashioned:* to believe or imagine that something is true; also, to like or approve of
32 *literary, old-fashioned:* a remark that is intended to injure someone or damage their reputation
33 a small unit of money used int the UK until 1971
34 *unusual:* looking like amethyst, a valuable purple stone used in jewellery
35 *formal:* a show of something such as money, power, or skill that is intended to impress people

and Jane developed a new way of bringing in the joint[36] so that this gage was evident. The elder Miss Maitland was aggrieved by it, and told my wife that servants ought not to wear rings. But my wife looked it up in *Enquire Within* and *Mrs. Motherly's Book of Household Management*, and found no prohibition. So Jane remained with this happiness added to her love.

The treasure of Jane's heart appeared to me to be what respectable people call a very deserving young man. 'William, ma'am,' said Jane one day suddenly, with ill-concealed **complacency**, as she counted out the beer bottles, 'William, ma'am, is a teetotaller[37]. Yes, m'm; and he don't smoke. Smoking, ma'am,' said Jane, as one who reads the heart, '*do* make such a dust about. Beside the waste of money. And the smell. However, I suppose they got to do it – some of theme. …'

William was at first a rather **shabby** young man of the ready-made black coat school of costume. He had watery grey eyes, and a complexion appropriate to the brother of one in a Home for the Dying. Euphemia did not fancy him very much, even at the beginning. His eminent respectability was **vouched for** by an alpaca[38] umbrella, from which he never allowed himself to be parted.

'He goes to chapel,' said Jane. 'His papa[39], ma'am–'

'His *what*, Jane?'

'His papa, ma'am, was Church[40]; but Mr. Maynard is a Plymouth Brother, and William thinks it Policy[41], ma'am, to go there too. Mr. Maynard comes and talks to him quite friendly when they ain't busy, about using up all the ends of string, and about his soul. He takes a lot of notice, do Mr. Maynard, of William, and the way he saves his soul, ma'am.'

Presently we heard that the head porter at Maynard's had left, and that William was head porter at twenty-three shillings a

36 a piece of meat
37 someone who never drinks alcohol
38 a South American animal like a llama; here, the soft cloth made from the animal's hair
39 *formal, old-fashioned:* a word meaning *father*, used in the past particualrly by the upper classes
40 Church of England
41 a principle or set of ideas that you think is sensible or wise

week. 'He is really kind of[42] over the man who drives the van,' said Jane, 'and him married, with three children.' And she promised in the pride of her heart to make interest for us with William to favour us so that we might get our parcels of drapery from Maynard's with exceptional promptitude.

After this promotion a rapidly increasing prosperity came upon Jane's young man. One day we learned that Mr. Maynard had given William a book. "*Smiles*' '*Elp Yourself*,' it's called,' said Jane; 'but it ain't comic. It tells you how to get on in the world, and some what William read to me was *lovely*, ma'am.'

Euphemia told me of this, laughing, and then she became suddenly **grave**. 'Do you know, dear,' she said, 'Jane said one thing I did not like. She had been quiet for a minute, and then she suddenly remarked, 'William is a lot above me, ma'am, ain't he?''

'I don't see anything in that,' I said, though later my eyes were to be opened.

One Sunday afternoon about that time I was sitting at my writing-desk – possibly I was reading a good book – when a something went by the window. I heard a **startled** exclamation behind me, and saw Euphemia with her hands clasped together and her eyes **dilated**. 'George,' she said in an awe-stricken[43] whisper, 'did you see?'

Then we both spoke to one another at the same moment, slowly and solemnly: 'A **silk** hat! *Yellow gloves!* A *new umbrella!*'

'It may be my fancy, dear,' said Euphemia; 'but his tie was very like yours. I believe Jane keeps him in ties. She told me a little while ago, in a way that implied volumes about the rest of your costume, 'The master *do* wear pretty ties, ma'am.' And he echoes all your novelties.'

The young couple passed our window again on their way to their customary walk. They were arm in arm. Jane looked exquisitely proud, happy, and uncomfortable, with new white cotton gloves, and William, in the silk hat, singularly genteel[44]!

42 *spoken, colloquial, phrase 'kind of'*: used when you are talking about someone or something in a general way without being very exact or definite
43 *Mostly literary, old-fashioned*: feeling extremely impressed by something
44 *old-fashioned, formal*: trying to appear as if you belong to a higher social class

That was the **culmination** of Jane's happiness. When she returned, 'Mr. Maynard has been talking to William, ma'am,' she said, 'and he is to serve customers, just like the young shop gentlemen, during the next sale. And if he gets on, he is to be made an assistant, ma'am, at the first opportunity. He has got to be as gentlemanly as he can, ma'am; and if he ain't, ma'am, he says it won't be for want of trying. Mr. Maynard has took a great fancy to him.'

'He *is* getting on, Jane,' said my wife.

'Yes, ma'am,' said Jane thoughtfully; 'he *is* getting on.'

And she sighed.

That next Sunday as I drank my tea I interrogated my wife. 'How is this Sunday different from all other Sundays, little woman? What has happened? Have you altered the curtains, or rearranged the furniture, or where is the indefinable difference of it? Are you wearing your hair in a new way without warning me? I perceive a change clearly, and I cannot for the life of me say what it is.'

Then my wife answered in her most tragic voice, 'George,' she said, 'that William has not come near the place to-day! And Jane is **crying her heart out** upstairs.'

There followed a period of silence. Jane, as I have said, stopped singing about the house, and began to care for our **brittle** possessions, which struck my wife as being a very sad sign indeed. The next Sunday, and the next, Jane asked to go out, 'to walk with William,' and my wife, who never attempts to extort confidences, gave her permission, and asked no questions. On each occasion Jane came back looking **flushed** and very determined. At last one day she became communicative.

'William is being led away,' she remarked abruptly, with a catching of the breath, **apropos** of tablecloths. 'Yes, m'm. She is a milliner, and she can play on the piano.'

'I thought,' said my wife, 'that you went out with him on Sunday.'

'Not out with him, m'm – after him. I walked along by the side of them, and told her he was engaged to me.'

'Dear me, Jane, did you? What did they do?'

'Took no more notice of me than if I was dirt. So I told her she should suffer for it.'

'It could not have been a very **agreeable** walk, Jane.'

'Not for no parties, ma'am.'

'I wish,' said Jane, 'I could play the piano, ma'am. But anyhow, I don't mean to let *her* get him away from me. She's older than him, and her hair ain't gold to the roots, ma'am.'

It was on the August Bank Holiday[45] that the crisis came. We do not clearly know the details of the fray[46], but only such fragments as poor Jane let fall. She came home dusty, excited, and with her heart hot within her.

The milliner's mother, the milliner, and William had made a party to the Art Museum at South Kensington, I think. Anyhow, Jane had calmly but firmly accosted them somewhere in the streets, and asserted her right to what, in spite of the consensus of literature, she held to be her inalienable property. She did, I think, go so far as to lay hands on him. They dealt with her in a **crushingly** superior way. They 'called a **cab**.' There was a 'scene'[47], William being pulled away into the four-wheeler[48] by his future wife and mother-in-law from the **reluctant** hands of our discarded Jane. There were threats of giving her 'in charge'[49].

'My poor Jane!' said my wife, **mincing** veal[50] as though she was mincing William. 'It's a shame[51] of them. I would think no more of him. He is not worthy of you.'

'No, m'm,' said Jane. 'He *is* weak.

'But it's that woman has done it,' said Jane. She was never known to bring herself to pronounce 'that woman's' name or to admit her girlishness[52]. 'I can't think what minds some women must have – to try and get a girl's young man away from her. But

45 a public holiday when shops, businesses and banks are closed
46 *old-fashioned:* a fight or argument
47 a noisy argument or strong show of feelings in public
48 a taxi/cab with four wheels, pulled by horses
49 to have arrested by the police
50 meat from a young cow
51 shameful
52 being and behaving like a girl, not a lady

there, it only hurts to talk about it,' said Jane.

Thereafter[53] our house rested from William. But there was something in the manner of Jane's **scrubbing** the front doorstep or sweeping out the rooms, a certain **viciousness**, that persuaded me that the story had not yet ended.

'Please, m'm, may I go and see a wedding to-morrow?' said Jane one day.

My wife knew by instinct whose wedding. 'Do you think it is wise, Jane?' she said.

'I would like to see the last of him,' said Jane.

'My dear,' said my wife, **fluttering** into my room about twenty minutes after Jane had started, 'Jane has been to the boot-hole[54] and taken all the left-off boots and shoes, and gone off to the wedding with them in a bag. Surely she cannot mean –'

'Jane,' I said, 'is developing character. Let us hope for the best.'

Jane came back with a pale, hard face. All the boots seemed to be still in her bag, at which my wife **heaved a** premature[55] **sigh** of relief. We heard her go upstairs and replace the boots with considerable emphasis.

'Quite a crowd at the wedding, ma'am,' she said presently, in a purely conversational style, sitting in our little kitchen and scrubbing the potatoes; 'and such a lovely day for them.' She proceeded to numerous other details, clearly avoiding some cardinal incident.

'It was all extremely respectable and nice, ma'am; but *her* father didn't wear a black coat, and looked quite out of place, ma'am. Mr. Piddingquirk –'

'*Who?*'

'Mr. Piddingquirk – William that was, ma'am – had white gloves, and a coat like a **clergyman**, and a lovely chrysanthemum. He looked so nice, ma'am. And there was red carpet down, just like for gentlefolks[56]. And they say he gave the clerk four

53 after a particular time that has been mentioned
54 a place like a cupboard for keeping boots and shoes
55 happening too soon
56 *old-fashioned:* people who come from families belonging to a high social class

shillings, ma'am. It was a real kerridge[57] they had – not a fly[58]. When they came out of church there was rice-throwing[59], and her two little sisters dropping dead flowers. And some one threw a slipper, and then I threw a boot –'

'Threw a *boot*, Jane!'

'Yes, ma'am. Aimed at her. But it hit *him*. Yes, ma'am, hard. Gev him a black eye, I should think. I only threw that one. I hadn't the heart to try again. All the little boys cheered when it hit him.'

After an interval – 'I am sorry the boot hit *him*.'

Another pause. The potatoes were being scrubbed violently. 'He always *was* a bit above me, you know, ma'am. And he was led away.'

The potatoes were more than finished. Jane rose sharply with a sigh, and rapped[60] the basin down on the table. 'I don't care,' she said.

'I don't care a rap. He will find out his mistake yet. It serves me right. I was stuck up about him. I ought not to have looked so high. And I am glad things are as things are.'

My wife was in the kitchen, seeing to the cookery. After the confession of the boot-throwing, she must have watched poor Jane **fuming** with a certain **dismay** in those brown eyes of hers. But I imagine they softened again very quickly, and then Jane's must have met them.

'Oh, ma'am,' said Jane, with an astonishing change of note, 'think of all that *might* have been! Oh, ma'am, I *could* have been so happy! I ought to have known, but I didn't know... . You're very kind to let me talk to you, ma'am ... for it's hard on me, ma'am ... it's har-r-r-d –'

And I gather that Euphemia so far forgot herself as to let Jane sob[61] out some of the fulness of her heart on a sympathetic shoulder. My Euphemia, thank Heaven, has never properly **grasped** the importance of 'keeping up her position.' And since

57 *pronunciation*: carriage (with roof)
58 an ordinary, simple two-person carriage without a roof pulled by horses
59 it is traditional to throw rice over the newly-married couple as they leave church
60 *old-fashioned*: to give a quick hard hit
61 *mostly literary*: to sob noisily while taking short breaths

that **fit** of weeping, much of the accent of bitterness has gone out of Jane's scrubbing and brush-work.

Indeed, something passed the other day with the butcher boy – but that scarcely belongs to this story. However, Jane is young still, and time and change are at work with her. We all have our sorrows, but I do not believe very much in the existence of sorrows that never heal.

Post-reading exercises

Understanding the story

1 Use these questions to help you check that you have understood the story.

1 Who is telling the story?
2 Who is Jane and why does the writer call her *our Jane*?
3 What did Jane use to sing? What were her *instruments*?
4 Why did the writer use to pray for silence? Does he want silence from Jane now?
5 Who is William? How long was Jane engaged to him?
6 How does the writer imagine that Jane and William first met?
7 Where does William work?
8 What does Jane wear to show that she is engaged?
9 What does Euphemia give Jane permission to do after she is engaged?
10 What does Euphemia think of William?
11 What makes William respectable in Jane's eyes?
12 What happens to William after he is promoted?
13 What is the book that Mr Maynard gives William and what is it about?
14 What is the comment Jane makes about William that Euphemia does not like?
15 How does William demonstrate his new wealth?
16 In what way is William going to be promoted in the future?
17 Why is Jane *crying her heart out* one Sunday?
18 Where does Jane go on the following two Sundays?
19 How does Jane describe William's new girlfriend?
20 How did the couple react when Jane told the girl she was engaged to William?
21 What happens on August Bank Holiday?
22 What advice does Euphemia give Jane?
23 What does Jane take with her to William's wedding?
24 What does Jane do at the wedding?
25 How does Jane react after the wedding? What is Euphemia's attitude?
26 Why is the writer optimistic about Jane's future?

Language study

Grammar

Multiple-clause sentences

In his longer, explanatory sentences, Wells uses a variety of ways to connect different clauses. For example, he uses conjunctions – words like *and*, *but*, *although* and *because*. He also uses punctuation such as dashes (–) to add information, and semi-colons (;) when the meaning of the clauses is closely connected.

1 Look at these examples from the story:

> *Jane was always very free with her conversation to my wife, and discoursed admirably in the kitchen on a variety of topics – so well, indeed, that I sometimes left my study door open – our house is a small one – to partake of it.*

We can break this sentence down into several clauses:

> *Jane was always very free with her conversation.*
> *(She) discoursed admirably on a variety of topics.*
> *I sometimes left my study door open to partake of it.*
> *Our house is a small one.*

2 Now answer the questions.

1 Wells uses a dash – to include extra information in his sentence. Where could he have used brackets ( ) instead of dashes?
2 Which conjunction does he use?
   Here is another example from the text:

> *But after William came, it was always William, nothing but William; William this and William that; and when we thought William was worked out and exhausted all together, then William all over again.*

3 What type of punctuation does Wells use in this sentence?
4 Which conjunctions does he use?
5 Break the sentence down into separate clauses.

> *As Euphemia has a reprehensible way of letting her servants talk to her, she soon heard of him.*

6 How many clauses are there in this sentence?

7 Which word is used to join the clauses? Could any other word(s) have been used?

3 **Join these clauses into single sentences using conjunctions and/or different punctuation. We have done the first one for you, as an example.**

1 I would like to attend the meeting. However, it's a little problematic.
I would like to attend the meeting; however, it's a little problematic.

2 Everybody was at the wedding. There were the Browns, the Pikes, the Collins family. Even Mr. Smith was there.

3 He is from quite a wealthy family. He never spends much on himself. He is very generous towards his friends.

4 I don't want them to stay with us. They could help us to paint the house. They always stay too long.

5 Rose is always very cheerful and positive. She has multiple sclerosis.

6 We tried everything. We looked in the drawers. We looked in the garage. We even looked in the attic. We could not find the papers anywhere.

7 Tim was watching TV. At the same time, Sue was studying.

8 Don't touch the paint. It's still wet!

Expressing purpose

The structure *so that* can be used to talk about purpose. In past sentences, *might* is occasionally used in a literary style. Look at these examples from the story:

> And presently, the amethystine ring was being worn about the house, even with ostentation, and Jane developed a new way of bringing in the joint, **so that** this gage was evident.
>
> And she promised in the pride of her heart to make interest for us with William to favour us **so that** we might get our parcels of drapery from Maynard's with exceptional promptitude.

4 Now answer the questions.

1 What does Jane do and why does she do it?
2 What does Jane promise to do? Why?
3 Which of these words could be used here instead of *might: could; should; may; would; can?*

Another way of expressing purpose is to use the infinitive of the verb. Here is an example from the story:

> *The next Sunday, and the next, Jane asked to go out 'to walk with William.*

4 Which infinitive expresses purpose? Rewrite the sentence using *so that.*

5 Rewrite the following sentences correctly, using the infinitive, or *could, should, may, would* or *can*.

1 She asked permission for to attend the dance.

_____

2 We ordered the new books well in advance so that we have them before Christmas.

_____

3 I'm going to the dentist tomorrow have my tooth out.

_____

4 Show me the brochure so that I could decide about our holiday.

_____

5 The students worked hard all week so that they can have the weekend off.

_____

6 Would you like to try the dress for see if it fits?

_____

7 Sam punished his son so that the boy will behave less selfishly.

_____

8 The babysitter is coming early so that we could go out.

_____

Such and so

Such

The words *such* (*a*) and *so* are easy to confuse.

Such is commonly used **before adjective + noun**, to emphasise the meaning of the adjective:

He is such a respectable young man [page 106]

Wells also uses it in a more literary way, **before abstract nouns**. In modern English, *such* is used before nouns but usually when they are 'gradable' and can be emphasised, eg mess, excitement, chaos.

Time was when I prayed ... for such silence ... such care [page 105]

So

So is used **before nouns without adjectives**:

He looked so nice ...
I could have been so happy ...

It is also used **before adverbs**:

Jane ... discoursed ... so well

There is also a structure with *so* **followed by adjective + *as* + infinitive**:

And I gather that Euphemia so far forgot herself as to let Jane sob out some of the fullness of her heart on a sympathetic shoulder.

This structure is formal and not commonly used.

6   Complete the sentences with *so* or *such* (*a/an*)

1   He's .... an attractive man!
2   Do you have to be .... negative about everything?
3   She played the violin .... beautifully.
4   Would you be .... kind as to pass me the salt?
5   They have .... good taste in furniture.
6   We ate .... much that we felt ill.
7   He has .... many books!
8   I've never met .... delightful people.
9   There was .... noise last night that it woke me up.
10 There was .... chaos during the airport strike.

Literary analysis

Plot

1 Look at these events from the story and number them in the correct order.
   a) Euphemia and her husband observe William in his new clothes.
   b) Jane cries and says she could have been happy with William.
   c) Jane follows William and is ignored by him and his girlfriend.
   d) Jane puts old shoes and boots into a bag.
   e) Jane throws a boot at William's bride.
   f) Jane wears her engagement ring around the house.
   g) Mr Maynard gives William a book.
   h) William does not come to the house to take Jane out.
   i) William escapes from Jane in a cab.
   j) William is promoted to head porter.

2 In what way is the plot 'circular'? How does the writer describe Jane at the beginning and the end of the narrative?

Character

3 Here are some words to describe Jane. Do you agree with them? What evidence is there in the story? Complete the list below, giving an example for each adjective. We have done the first two for you, as examples.

brave – *for example, she follows William and challenges him in front of his girlfriend*

careless – *for example, she breaks things belonging to her employers*

tactful

opinionated

optimistic

trusting

self-respecting

respectable

naïve

proud

4 How would you describe the writer of the story? Think about his attitude to his wife, the servants and Jane's situation. What does the last paragraph of the story tell you about him?

5 How would you describe Euphemia? What is her relationship with:
   a) her husband
   b) the servants?

Narration

6 The story is written from the point of view of the master of the house, George. How would you describe his attitude to the events that occur?

7 Wells uses various devices to make it possible for his narrator to find out what is happening. For example, the first meeting between Jane and William is invented or imagined. Look at the last few paragraphs of the story (from My *wife was in the kitchen* ... [page 112]) and find more examples of George drawing conclusions or imagining events. Look for sentences containing these verbs: *fancy, imagine, gather*.

8 How does George know that Jane enjoys talking about different topics?

9 Is George always present at the conversations between Jane and Euphemia? Where does he get his information?

10 Is Wells sympathetic to his narrator? Is George always right in his interpretation of events?

11 How are differences in social class portrayed in the story?

Atmosphere

12 What is your impression of George and Euphemia's house and the way it is run? For example, is it calm or chaotic? Is it tidy or untidy? Is it quiet or noisy? Give reasons for your answer.

13 What kind of atmosphere is created in the conversations between Euphemia and Jane? How does Wells create this effect?

14 Is the story humorous, sad or a mixture of both? Has it got a happy ending?

Style

15 Wells's narrator, George, sometimes writes in long, rather formal sentences. What effect does this have? How does it affect your ideas about George?

16 Is the dialogue realistic? What do you think of the way Wells portrays Jane's accent and dialect?

17 The story is quite typical of the kind of story published in newspapers at the time. Why do you think this kind of story was popular?

18 Choose a scene and write some dialogue to accompany it, for example, the scene where William and Jane meet; one of the confrontations between Jane; William and the milliner; the scene at the wedding.

Guidance to the above literary terms, answer keys to all the exercises and activities, plus a wealth of other reading-practice material, can be found on the student's section of the Macmillan Readers website at: www.macmillanenglish.com/readers.

A Christmas Song
by H E Bates

About the author

Herbert Ernest Bates was born in 1905 in Rushden, Northamptonshire, in the Midlands of England. Known as 'H E' from a young age, Bates was educated at Kettering Grammar School and after leaving, he worked as a journalist and a clerk on a local newspaper.

From an early age, Bates knew that he wanted to be a writer. He published his first book, *The Two Sisters*, when he was 20. In the next 15 years, he acquired great popularity with his stories about English country life. He loved the rural areas of the Midlands and went for long walks there, often at night.

In 1931, Bates married Madge Cox, whom he had known since he was a boy. They moved to Kent where they raised their four children. Their house, where Bates lived all his life, had an acre of garden in which he took great pleasure, and he also wrote books about plants and flowers.

During World War II, Bates was a Squadron Leader in the Royal Air Force. He was commissioned by the RAF to write stories about the war. Some of his stories of service life, such as *How Sleep the Brave* (1943), were written under the pseudonym of 'Flying Officer X'. They were first published in the *News Chronicle* and later appeared in book form as *The Greatest People in the World* and *How Sleep the Brave*. Bates was then posted to the Far East. He wrote two novels about Burma, *The Purple Plain* and *The Jacaranda Tree*, and another set in India, *The Scarlet Sword*.

After the war, Bates continued to write, and produced, on average, one novel and a collection of short stories every year. In 1958, *The Darling Buds of May* was published, the first in a series of popular novels about a country family called the Larkins. After Bates died, this book was made into a TV series by his son, Richard. Many other stories were adapted for TV and others for films. The most famous are, perhaps, *The Purple Plain* starring Gregory Peck, and *The Triple Echo*.

H E Bates died in 1974, having written more than 100 novels and collections of short stories. He also wrote essays, plays and a story for children, *The White Admiral* (1968). Described by Graham Greene as 'Britain's successor to Chekhov', he was successful and respected in his lifetime. However, perhaps his greatest success came after his death with the TV adaptations of *The Darling Buds of May* and its sequel, *My Uncle Silas*. His works have been translated into many languages.

About the story

A Christmas Song was first published in 1950 in *Woman's Own* magazine. In 1951, it was included in the collection *Colonel Julian and Other Stories* under the title *A Song to Remember*.

Background information

Evensford

The town where the story takes place is based on Bates's home town of Rushden. It is his first use of the name which appears again in some of his later fiction.

Evensford is an industrial Midlands town with *many hilly little streets above the river*, and a gasworks[1]. There must also be a leather factory, as the Williamson family in the story are successful leather manufacturers.

Music

At the time the story was written, music shops sold sheet music and gramophone records. In the shop where Clara works, there are *gramophone cubicles*, where customers can listen to records before buying them. Clara sells *jazz sheet music* to the factory workers, and the author mentions Danny Kaye, an American comedy actor who had several 'hits' in the 1950s with light-hearted songs for children. These would have been particularly popular at Christmas.

Schubert

Franz Schubert (1797–1828) was an Austrian composer. He wrote opera, symphonies, liturgical music and over 600 *lieder*. A *lied* is a European romantic song, typically arranged for a single singer and piano. The song which features in the story is Schubert's *Standchen*.

1   a factory where gas for fuel is produced

Summary

It may help you to know something about what happens in the story before you read it. Don't worry, this summary does not tell you how the story ends!

Clara is a talented young music teacher who works in a music shop in a small Midlands town. Every Christmas, she hopes that it will snow so that the town will look prettier. She has a sister, Effie, who is not so talented but is much more popular with the young men of the town.

Every Christmas, the Williamsons, a family of successful leather manufacturers, hold a big party to which Clara, Effie, and their parents are always invited. Clara decides that this year, she will not go, as she never enjoys it. Effie insists that she must go and warns Clara that the Williamsons will force her to go in the end.

On the night of the party, a young man comes to the music shop. He wants a particular song but he cannot remember the name or the composer. Clara sings several songs, but none is the correct one. She asks if it is a love song and the man says it is. Clara encourages the man to return to the shop if he remembers the tune.

At nine o'clock, Clara is sitting at the piano in her dressing gown[2] when one of the Williamson sons, Freddy, arrives and insists on being let in. Clara gives him a drink and he tries to kiss her and touch her. Clara finally agrees to go to the party with him. As they are leaving, the young man (who had been looking for the song) appears again at the door. He has remembered some of the words to the song. Clara sits at the piano and plays the song, which is by Schubert. Freddy is angry and goes out to sit in the car. Clara finds the record for the young man, who is very grateful. Will Clara go to the party?

Pre-reading exercises

Key vocabulary

This section will help you familiarise yourself with some of the more specific vocabulary used in the story. You may want to use it to help you before you start reading, or as a revision exercise after you have finished the story.

2   a robe like a long loose coat that you typically wear before dressing

Vocabulary connected with music

Clara works in a music shop in England around the mid-20th century. Here is some of the vocabulary from the story which is related to music.

1 Match the words in the box below to the correct definitions.

1	**voice-training**	a) to make musical sounds with your lips closed
2	**sheet-music**	b) (old fashioned) a machine for playing records
3	**to hum**	c) one of the sections in a line of music; each contains several notes
4	**carol**	d) a series of musical notes in a fixed order from the lowest to the highest, or the highest to the lowest
5	**bar**	e) learning how to sing
6	**record**	f) a traditional song sung at Christmas
7	**gramophone**	g) a large round black piece of plastic containing music or other sounds
8	**scale**	h) music printed on pages that do not form part of a book

2 Complete this paragraph with an appropriate word from the box above.

At Christmas, the most popular songs are, of course, ... When I was a child in the 50s, I remember my mother .... 'Silent Night' as she moved about the kitchen. She had had no professional .... but she was an excellent singer and pianist. Every day she practised her .... , playing from low notes to high and back again. On Christmas Day, she would take out the .... from the drawer, sit down at the piano and play the first .... of our favourite songs. The whole family would then break into song. When mother was tired, she would stop playing and we would open up the .... and put on the .... we had bought each other for Christmas.

Winter weather

It is Christmas time in the story and Clara is hoping for snow. The vocabulary below describes different aspects of the weather and the winter landscape.

3 **Look at the definitions in the box below, then answer the questions that follow.**

> **frost** a thin white layer of ice that looks like powder and forms on things outside when the weather is very cold
>
> **crisp** (adj) firm, dry and fresh
>
> **to glisten** if something glistens, it shines because it is wet or covered with oil
>
> **to glitter** to shine with a lot of small quick flashes of light
>
> **to sparkle** to shine with small points of reflected light
>
> **to crackle** to make continuous short sounds like the sound of wood burning

Look at the verbs which mean *to shine*? Which of the verbs would you use to describe the following:

a) pieces of broken glass in the sunlight

b) someone's skin after they have been running fast

c) the noise of frost under your feet

Verbs describing actions

The factory owner's son, Freddy Williamson, is portrayed as a clumsy[3], loud and vulgar young man. Look at these verbs which are used to describe his actions.

> **to bawl** to shout in a loud angry way
>
> **to stamp** to put your feet down hard and noisily on something
>
> **to grasp** to take and hold something or someone tightly
>
> **to smack** to make a loud noise with your lips and tongue
>
> **to stump** to walk hitting the ground hard with your feet as you go
>
> **to blunder** to move in a careless way, creating problems as you go
>
> **to seize** to suddenly and firmly hold something or someone by a part of their body or clothing

4 **Now find the verbs in the story, and write an example of how each is used below.**

to bawl   *Freddy Williamson had bawled out 'Good old Clara!'*

to stamp
_____

3 moves in a way that is not graceful, and breaks things or knocks against them

to grasp

to smack

to stump

to blunder

to seize

5 Write your own sentences, using the verbs above.

Colloquial expressions and 'slang'

The author uses a lot of colloquial expressions and 'slang' in this story. 'Slang' describes words or expressions that are very informal and are not considered suitable for more formal situations. Some slang is used only by a particular group of people. In this story, the author has used slang expressions so that the characters' speech sounds colloquial and therefore is more authentic and real. Many of these expressions are still used in everyday English. Some examples are listed below. Some have a similar meaning; some are rude. You may have heard them before in general conversation or in films.

> **go to hell** *slang, impolite* used for telling someone angrily to stop annoying you
> **fair enough** *colloquial, polite* used for saying that you understand and accept what is being said
> **damn** + adjective/noun, used for emphasis or intensifying, meaning 'really' or 'very'. This is colloquial, rather than slang, and is still used in modern English. For example: – 'damn cheek' used to describe someone's behaviour or comment as rude or disrespectful; – 'damn glad' means very pleased
> **cool** *slang* calm, relaxed, fashionable; used as a compliment by young people; (in this story, it means 'very impertinent/cheeky'). Other modern uses for the word 'cool' include 'be cool' and 'stay cool' meaning to tell someone to be or remain calm; and 'cool!' meaning 'fine' or 'okay'
> **Let the blinds up!** *slang; unusual* a way of telling someone to lose their inhibitions, used to encourage someone to relax and be more open
> **Let yourself go!** *slang* allow yourself to feel and express emotions without trying to control them
> **Snap out of it!** *slang, colloquial* make an effort to stop being unhappy, upset, overly thoughtful or worried
> **Get ready!** *colloquial* prepare yourself (to go out, to run a race, etc)
> **Good old ...** *colloquial, friendly* used before the name of someone or something that always does what you want or expect
> **How did it go?** *colloquial* enquiring about an event in the past, perhaps something that the person was worried about
> **awful / awfully** + adjective/noun *old-fashioned* used for emphasis, eg 'an awful bind', 'awfully silly' meaning 'very'

6 Choose one of the expressions above to complete the following sentences.

Bill was daydreaming again, staring into the distance. He was obviously worried about something. '...................... !', said Laurie. Bill had had a shower and was still wearing his wet towel around his waist. 'And for goodness sake, Bill,...................... ! 'We're going to be late!' But Bill did not want to hurry, and he was sick of listening to Laurie complaining. '...................... !' he mumbled. 'All right, all right!' said Laurie, '...................... ! You've been so tense lately. You need to relax – let's get to this party and you can .... You know you need it!' Bill knew she was right – he should relax and have some fun.

'...................... , sorry', he said. And he went upstairs to get dressed.

'...................... Bill', said Laurie, '– always gets ready eventually!'

Main themes

Before you read the story, you may want to think about some of its main themes. The questions will help you think about the story as you are reading it for the first time. There is more discussion of the main themes in the *Literary analysis* section after the story.

Life in a small, industrial town

Bates gives us a brief but convincing portrayal of life in Evensford and its class structure. The factory workers are described as *long columns of working class mackintoshes*; the *gentlemen* of the town play billiards and card games in the club; the factory owners, in this case the Williamsons, are prosperous and dominate the social scene with their annual Christmas party.

7 As you read the story, ask yourself:

a) How does a young woman like Clara fit into the social structure of Evensford?

b) Would Clara be happier living somewhere else?

Cultural aspirations

Clara longs for a change from the monotony of life in Evensford. She is a trained musician but there are not many opportunities for her to share her interests. In general, the customers at the shop are not very unadventurous, and always ask for the same type of music. Her songs are not fully appreciated or understood. She escapes in her mind by imagining Evensford as an Alpine[4] town covered in snow, and herself as a singer of Mozart to an appreciative audience.

8 As you read the story, ask yourself:

a) Is Bates's portrayal of the limitations of small-town culture convincing?

b) What does he suggest about the cultural aspirations of most of the people in Evensford?

Romance

When a young man appears in the music shop asking for a love song, Clara makes every effort to help him. He is shy and admires her talent. He is, in fact, the complete opposite of Freddy Williamson, the factory owner's son who tries to seduce Clara in a clumsy and insensitive fashion. Clara does not enjoy Freddy's attentions, but she does not completely reject them either. She lives in a world of her own, in which everything is more refined and romantic.

9 As you read the story, ask yourself:

a) What kind of person does Clara want to fall in love with?

b) Is the young man who comes to the shop attracted to Clara?

Christmas

The story takes place at Christmas time, a festival full of traditions – religious, cultural and family-orientated. It is a time associated with 'good will', peace, and hope. It is also associated with being kind to others. Christmas celebrates the birth of Jesus and many people go to church and sing carols to mark the occasion. Traditionally, Christmas is an occasion for families to share food and gifts, and spend time together. It is also a time of parties and festivities. Some families enjoy a quiet Christmas, and prefer to spend time together at home; others prefer to go out and celebrate with friends and neighbours. In the US

---

4   relating to high mountains, particularly those in the European Alps

and the UK, 'a white Christmas' is a traditional image, and people enjoy the anticipation of waiting to see if there will be snow or not.

The story describes various features and styles of Christmas, and we see it from various points of view – Clara wonders about snow, and for her, it's a time of longing and wondering about the future. Freddy sees it as an excuse to have a party. Effie can get attention for her singing. As you read the story, think about the different attitudes and atmospheres of Christmas that Bates describes.

A Christmas Song

by H E Bates

She gave lessons in the long room above the music shop. Her pupils won many examinations[5] and were afterwards very successful at local concerts and sometimes in giving lessons in voice-training to other pupils. She herself had won many examinations and everybody said how brilliant she was.

Every Christmas, as this year, she longed for snow. It gave a **transfiguring** gay[6] distinction to a town that otherwise had none. It lifted up the squat[7] little shops, built of red brick with upper storeys of terra-cotta[8]; it made the roofs down the hill like glistening cakes; it even gave importance to the stuffy **gauze**-windowed club where local gentlemen played billiards and solo whist[9] over **meagre** portions of watered whisky. One could imagine, with the snow, that one was in Bavaria or Vienna or the Oberland, and that horse-drawn sleighs, of which she read in travel guides, would glide gracefully down the ugly hill from the gasworks. One could imagine Evensford, with its many hilly little streets above the river, a little Alpine town. One could imagine anything. Instead there was almost always rain and long columns of dreary working-class mackintoshes[10] floating down a street that was like a **dreary** black canal. Instead of singing Mozart to the snow she spent long hours selling jazz sheet-music to factory workers and earned her reward, at last, on Christmas Eve, by being bored at the Williamsons' party.

Last year she had sung several songs at the Williamsons' party. Some of the men, who were getting **hearty** on mixtures of gin

5 an unusual way of saying *pass an examination*; Bates may be suggesting that Clara has won competitions
6 *old-fashioned*: happy and excited
7 wide and not very tall or high
8 a brown-red clay used for making bowls, plates, roofs and houses
9 a card game
10 *old-fashioned*: a coat that stops you getting wet in the rain

and port wine, had applauded in the wrong places, and Freddy Williamson had bawled out 'Good old Clara!'

She knew the men preferred Effie. Her sister was a very **gay** person although she did not sing; she had never passed an examination in her life, but there was, in a strange way, hardly anything you felt she could not do. She had a character like a chameleon[11]; she had all the love affairs. She laughed a great deal, in rippling **infectious** scales, so that she made other people begin laughing, and she had large violet-blue eyes. Sometimes she laughed so much that Clara herself would begin weeping[12].

This year Clara was not going to the Williamsons' party; she had made up her mind. The Williamsons were in leather[13]; they were very successful and had a large early Edwardian house with **bay-windows** and corner cupolas[14] and bathroom windows of stained glass overlooking the river.

They were fond of giving parties several times a year. Men who moved only in Rotarian[15] or golf circles turned up with wives whose corset suspenders[16] could be seen like bulging pimples under sleek dresses. About midnight Mrs Williamson grew rowdy and began rushing from room to room making love[17] to other men. The two Williamson boys, George and Freddy, became **rowdy** too, and took off their jackets and did muscular and noisy gymnastics with the furniture.

At four o'clock she went upstairs to close the windows of the music-room and pull the curtains and make up the fire. It was raining in misty delicate drops and the air was not like Christmas. In the garden there were lime trees and their dark red branches, washed with rain, were like glowing veins in the deep blue air.

11 someone who changes their opinions, ideas or behaviour to fit any situation; a type of lizard whose skin changes colour to match the colours around it
12 crying because you are unhappy or experience another strong emotion
13 in the leather manufacturing trade
14 a part of a roof shaped like half a ball, often covered in shiny material
15 Rotary Club: a local club that is part of Rotary International, a charity whose members are business people or local people
16 the buttons on a woman's stockings
17 *old-fashioned:* to flirt or speak in a romantic way to someone

As she was coming out of the room her sister came upstairs.

'Oh! There you are. There's a young man downstairs who wants a song and doesn't know the name.'

'It's probably a Danny Kaye[18]. It always is.'

'No it isn't. He says it's a Christmas song.'

'I'll come,' she said. Then half-way downstairs she stopped; she remembered what it was she was going to say to Effie. 'By the way, I'm not coming to the party,' she said.

'Oh! Clara, you promised. You always come.'

'I know; but I'm tired, and I don't feel like coming and there it is.'

'The Williamsons will never let you **get away with** it,' her sister said. 'They'll drag you by force.'

'I'll see about this song,' she said. 'What did he say it was?'

'He says it's a Christmas song. You'll never get away with it. They'll never let you.'

She went down into the shop. Every day people came into the shop for songs whose names they did not know. 'It goes like this,' they would say, 'or it goes like that.' They would try humming a few notes and she would take it up from them; it was always something popular, and in the end, with practice, it was never very difficult.

A young man in a brown overcoat with a brown felt hat and an umbrella stood by the sheet-music counter. He took off his hat when she came up to him.

'There was a song I wanted –'

'A **carol**?' she said.

'No, a song,' he said. 'A Christmas song'

He was very nervous and kept rolling the ferrule[19] of the umbrella on the floor linoleum. He wetted his lips and would not look at her.

'If you could remember the words?'

'I'm afraid I can't.'

'How does it go? Would you know that?'

He opened his mouth either as if to begin singing a few notes

18 a song by Danny Kaye, the American singer and comedian
19 a piece of metal or rubber fixed to the end of a stick to prevent it being damaged

or to say something. But nothing happened and he began biting his lip instead.

'If you could remember a word or two,' she said. 'Is it a new song?'

'You see, I think it's German,' he said.

'Oh,' she said. 'Perhaps it's by Schubert?'

'It sounds awfully silly, but I simply don't know. We only heard it once,' he said.

He seemed about to put on his hat. He ground the ferrule of the umbrella into the linoleum[20]. Sometimes it happened that people were too shy even to hum the notes of the song they wanted, and suddenly she said:

'Would you care to come upstairs? We might find it there.'

Upstairs in the music room she sang the first bars of one or two songs by Schubert. She sat at the piano and he stood respectfully at a distance, leaning on the umbrella, too shy to interrupt her. She sang a song by Brahms and he listened hopefully. She asked him if these were the songs, but he shook his head, and finally, after she had sung another song by Schubert, he blurted out:

'You see, it isn't actually a Christmas song. It is, and it isn't. It's more that it makes you think of Christmas –'

'Is it a love song?'

'Yes.'

She sang another song by Schubert; but it was not the one he wanted; and at last she stood up. 'You see, there are so many love songs – '

'Yes, I know, but this one is rather different somehow.'

'Couldn't you bring her in?' she said. 'Perhaps she would remember?'

'Oh! No,' he said. 'I wanted to find it without that.'

They went downstairs and several times on the way down he thanked her for singing. 'You sing beautifully,' he said. 'You would have liked this song.'

'Come in again if you think of it,' she said. 'If you can only think of two or three bars.'

Nervously he **fumbled** with the umbrella and then quickly

20 a hard flat substance with a shiny surface used for covering floors

put on his hat and then as quickly took it off again. He thanked her for being so kind, raising his hat a second time. Outside the shop he put up the umbrella too sharply, and a breeze, catching it, twisted him on the bright pavement and bore him out of sight.

Rain fell gently all evening and customers came in and shook wet hats on bright pianos. She walked about trying to think of the song the young man wanted. Songs by Schubert went through her head and became mixed with the sound of carols from cubicles[21] and she was glad when the shop had closed.

Effie began racing about in her underclothes, getting ready for the party. 'Clara, you can't mean it that you're not coming.'

'I do mean it. I'm always bored and they really don't want me.'

'They love you.'

'I can't help it. I made up my mind last year. I never enjoy it, and they'll be better without me.'

'They won't let you get away with it,' Effie said. 'I warn you they'll come and fetch you.'

At eight o'clock her father and mother drove off with Effie in the Ford[22]. She went down through the shop and unbolted the front door and let them out into the street. 'The stars are shining,' her mother said. 'It's getting colder.' She stood for a second or two in the doorway, looking up at the stars and thinking that perhaps, after all, there was a touch of frost in the air.

'Get ready!' Effie called from the car. 'You know what the Williamsons are!' and laughed with high infectious scales so that her mother and father began laughing too.

After the car had driven away she bolted the door and switched off the front shop bell. She went upstairs and put on her dressing-gown and tried to think once again of the song the young man had wanted. She played over several songs on the piano, singing them softly.

At nine o'clock something was thrown against the sidestreet

21 a small enclosed area in a room, separated from the rest of the room by thin walls or curtains
22 a make of car

window and she heard Freddy Williamson bawling:

'Who isn't coming to the party? Open the window.'

She went to the window and pulled back the curtain and stood looking down. Freddy Williamson stood in the street below and threw his driving gloves at her.

'Get dressed! Come on!'

She opened the window.

'Freddy, be quiet. People can hear.'

'I want them to hear. Who isn't coming to whose party? I want them to hear.'

He threw the driving gloves up at the window again.

'Everybody is insulted!' he said. 'Come on.'

'Please,' she said.

'Let me in then!' he bawled. 'Let me come up and talk to you.'

'All right,' she said.

She went downstairs and let him in through the shop and he came up to the music room shivering, stamping enormous feet. 'Getting colder,' he kept saying. 'Getting colder.'

'You should put on an overcoat,' she said.

'Never wear one,' he said. 'Can't bear to be stuffed up[23].'

'Then don't grumble because you're starved to death.'

He stamped up and down the room, a square-boned young man with enormous lips and pink flesh and small poodle[24]-like eyes, pausing now and then to rub his hands before the fire.

'The Mater[25] sends orders you're to come back with me,' he said, 'and she absolutely won't take no for an answer.'

'I'm not coming,' she said.

'Of course you're coming! I'll have a drink while you get ready.'

'I'll pour you a drink,' she said, 'but I'm not coming. What will you have?'

---

23 wrapped up tightly so that you cannot breathe
24 a dog with thick curly fur
25 *old-fashioned:* mother

'Gin' he said. 'Clara, sometimes you're the most awful bind[26].'

She poured the drink, not answering. Freddy Williamson lifted the glass and said:

'Sorry, didn't mean that. Happy Christmas. Good old Clara.'

'Happy Christmas.'

'Good old Clara. Come on, let's have one[27] for Christmas.'

Freddy Williamson put **clumsy** hands across her shoulders, kissing her with lips rather like those of a heavy wet dog.

'Good old Clara,' he said again. 'Good old girl.'

Songs kept crossing and recrossing her mind, bewildering her into moments of dreamy distraction. She had the feeling of trying to grasp something that was floating away.

'Don't stand there like a dream,' Freddy Williamson, said 'Put some clothes on. Come on.'

'I'm going to tie up Christmas presents and then go to bed.'

'Oh! Come on, Clara, come on. Millions of chaps[28] are there, waiting.'

She stood dreamily in the centre of the room, thinking of the ardent[29] shy young man who could not remember the song.

'You're such a dream,' Freddy Williamson said. 'You just stand there. You've got to snap out of yourself.'

Suddenly he pressed himself against her in attitudes of muscular, heavier love, grasping her about the waist, partly lifting her from the floor, his lips wet on her face.

'Come on, Clara,' he kept saying, 'let the blinds up[30]. Can't keep the blinds down for ever.'

'Is it a big party?'

'Come on, let the blinds up.'

'How can I come to the party if you keep holding me here?'

'Let the blinds up and come to the party too,' he said. 'Eh?'

'No.'

'Well, once more kiss,' he said. He smacked at her lips with

26 to be annoying, difficult or not convenient
27 refers here to a kiss
28 *British, old-fashioned:* a man, especially one you like
29 *literary:* showing very strong feelings of love towards someone
30 *colloquial:* a way of telling someone to lose their inhibitions

his heavy dog-like mouth, pressing her body backwards. 'Good old Clara. All you got to do is let yourself go. Come on – let the blinds up. Good old Clara.'

'All right. Let me get my things on,' she said. 'Get yourself another drink while you're waiting.'

'Fair enough. Good old Clara.'

While she went away to dress he drank gin and stumped about the room. She came back in her black coat with a black and crimson scarf on her head and Freddy Williamson said: 'Whizzo[31]. That's better. Good old Clara,' and kissed her again, running clumsy **ruffling** hands over her face and neck and hair.

When they went downstairs someone was tapping lightly on the glass of the street door. 'Police for the car,' Freddy Williamson said. 'No lights or some damn[32] thing,' but when she opened the door it was the young man who could not remember the song. He stood there already raising his hat:

'I'm terribly sorry. Oh! You're going out. Excuse me.'

'Did you remember it?' she said.

'Some of it,' he said. 'The words.'

'Come in a moment,' she said.

He came in from the street and she shut the door. It was dark in the shop, and he did not seem so nervous. He began to say: 'It goes rather like this – I can't remember it all. But something like this – *Leise flehen meine Lieder – Liebchen, komm zu mir –* '

'It is by Schubert,' she said.

She went across the shop and sat down at one of the pianos and began to sing it for him. She heard him say, 'That's it. That's the one,' and Freddy Williamson **fidgeted** with the latch[33] of the shop door as he kept one hand on it, impatient to go.

'It's very beautiful,' the young man said. 'It's not a Christmas song, but somehow –'

Freddy Williamson stamped noisily into the street, and a second or two later she heard him start up the car. The door-catch rattled where he had left it open and a current of cold air blew into the dark shop.

31 *old-fashioned:* an expression of approval
32 *impolite:* used for emphasis, especially when we are annoyed about something
33 a metal object for keeping a door fastened shut

She had broken off her singing because, after the first verse, she could not remember the words. *Softly fly my song – Loved one, come to me* – she was not sure how it went after that.

'I'm sorry I can't remember the rest,' she said.

'It's very kind of you,' he said. The door irritated her by banging on its catch. She went over and shut it and out in the street Freddy Williamson blew impatiently on the horn of the car.

'Was it the record you wanted?' she said. 'There is a very good one –'

'If it's not too much trouble.'

'I think I can find it,' she said. 'I'll put on the light.'

As she looked for the record and found it, she sang the first few bars of it again. 'There is great tenderness in it,' she began to say. 'Such a wonderful tenderness,' but suddenly it seemed as if the young man was embarrassed. He began fumbling in his pocket-book[34] for his money, but she said, 'Oh! No. Pay after Christmas. Pay any time,' and at the same moment Freddy Williamson opened the door of the shop and said:

'What goes on[35]? After hours[36], after hours. Come on.'

'I'm just coming,' she said.

'I'll say good night,' the young man said. 'I'm very grateful. I wish you a Happy Christmas.'

'Happy Christmas,' she said.

Outside the stars were green and sharp in a sky without wind; the street had dried except for dark prints of frost on pavements.

'Damn cool[37],' Freddy Williamson kept saying 'Damn cool.'

He drove rather fast, silent and a little sulky, out towards the high ground overlooking the river. Rain had been falling everywhere through all the first weeks of December and now as the car came out on the valley edge she could see below her a great pattern of winter floodwater, the hedgerows cutting it into

34 wallet
35 happens
36 after closing time; after the time when a place such as a bar or a shop usually closes
37 here, used to mean impertinent, cheeky

rectangular lakes glittering with green and yellow lights from towns on the far side.

'I'd have told him to go to hell,' Freddy Williamson said. 'I call it damn cool. Damn cool.'

'See the floods,' she said. 'There'll be skating[38].'

'The damn cheek people have,' Freddy Williamson said. 'Damn cheek.'

He drove the car with **sulky** abandon into the gravel drive of the big Edwardian house. Dead chestnut leaves swished away on all sides, harsh and **brittle**, and she could see frost white on the edges of the big lawn.

'One before we go in,' Freddy Williamson said. She turned away her mouth but he caught it with clumsy **haste**, like a dog **seizing** a bird. 'Good old Clara. Let the blinds up. It's Christmas Eve.'

'Put the car away and I'll wait for you,' she said.

'Fair enough,' he said. 'Anything you say. Good old Clara. Damn glad you come.'

She got out of the car and stood for a few moments looking down the valley. She bent down and put her hands on the grass. Frost was crisp and hard already, and she could see it sparkling brightly on tree branches and on rain-soaked stems[39] of dead flowers. It made her breath glisten in the house-lights coming across the lawn. It seemed to be **glittering** even on the long wide floodwaters, so that she almost persuaded herself the valley was one great river of ice already, wonderfully transformed.

Standing there, she thought of the young man, with his shy ardent manner, his umbrella and his raised hat. The song he had not been able to remember began to go through her head again – *Softly fly my songs* – *Loved one, come to me* –; but at that moment Freddy Williamson came blundering[40] up the drive and seized her once again like a hungry dog.

---

38 the activity of moving around on ice, wearing special shoes with a blade called ice-skates

39 the long thin central part of a plant from which the flowers and leaves grow

40 *old-fashioned, literary:* extremely careless or stupid

'One before we go in,' he said. 'Come on. Good old Clara. One before we go in. Good show[41].'

Shrieks of laughter came suddenly from the house as if someone, perhaps her sister, had ignited little fires of merriment that were crackling at the windows.

'Getting worked up!' Freddy Williamson said. 'Going to be good!'

She felt the frost crackling under her feet. She grasped at something that was floating away. *Leise flehen meine Lieder – Oh! my loved one* – how did it go?

41 *old-fashioned, colloquial:* very good, well done

Post-reading exercises

Understanding the story

1 **Use these questions to help you check that you have understood the story.**

1 What is Clara's job? Where does she work?
2 What time of year is it?
3 What does Clara want to happen? What difference will it make to the town?
4 What did Clara do last Christmas?
5 Who is Effie and how is she different to Clara?
6 Who are the Williamsons? What has Clara decided in connection with their party?
7 What does Effie mean when she says *You'll never get away with it?*
8 What does the young man in the brown overcoat want?
9 Why does Clara go upstairs? Does she find what the young man wants?
10 When do Effie and her parents leave for the party?
11 Why does Freddy Williamson come to Clara's house? What is his attitude towards Clara?
12 Who arrives when Clara and Freddy are leaving for the party? What does he want?
13 Why is Freddy annoyed?
14 What does Freddy do when they arrive at the party?
15 What does Clara do while Freddy is putting the car away? What does she think about?

Language study

Punctuation: the use of the semi-colon

Semi-colons (;) are often used instead of full stops, in cases where sentences are grammatically independent, but where the meaning is closely connected.

1 **Look at the second paragraph of the story** [page 13] **and answer the questions:**

> *It lifted up the squat little shops, built of red brick with upper storeys of terra-cotta; it made the roofs down the hill like glistening cakes; it even gave importance to the stuffy gauze-windowed club where local gentlemen played billiards and solo whist over meagre portions of watered whisky.*

a) How many sentences are there?
b) What does *it* refer to at the beginning of each sentence?
c) How are the sentences connected? Do they have similar themes?

Now look at the fourth paragraph [page 132].

d) Where does the author use semi-colons?
e) How is the meaning of the sentences connected?

Phrasal verbs and idiomatic expressions

Bates often uses phrasal verbs, which tend to make a text sound more informal. These verbs sometimes form part of an idiomatic expression. Look at these examples from the story:

> *This year Clara was not going to the Williamsons' party; she had made up her mind.*
> *Men **turned up** … with wives whose corset suspenders could be seen like bulging pimples under sleek dresses.*
> *'The Williamson's will never **let you get away with it**,' her sister said.*

To make up one's mind means to decide something.

What is the meaning of *to turn up* and *to let someone get away with something*?

2 **Write a suitable form of one of the verbs or expressions in the sentences below.**

| pull back   snap out of   let yourself go   break off   turn away |
| put away   get out of |

1 He told her to relax and .... herself ....
2 It was so cold outside that she did not want to .... the car.
3 When I had looked at the photographs, I .... the album .... in a drawer.
4 It was very dark in the room so he .... the curtains to let the sunshine in.
5 The girl was in a dream and could not .... it.
6 They had been laughing, but they .... and fell silent when he came into the room.
7 When Freddy tried to kiss her, Clara .... her face ....

Literary analysis

Plot

1 What kind of place is Evensford? Why do you think Bates writes so much about what it *would* look like in the snow?

2 When do we first learn the name of the main character in the story? Why do you think Bates waits so long to tell us her name?

3 Does Effie have a big part in the story? Why do you think she is included?

4 What impression of the Williamson's does Bates give us in paragraph 5 [page 132]?

5 How does Bates describe the young man who is looking for a song? What is your impression of him?

6 Why do you think Clara takes trouble to help the young man?

7 Look again at the paragraph where Bates describes the young man's departure from the shop [pages 134–5]. What impression does this give?

8 How does Freddy Williamson arrive at Clara's house? What are his motives for coming to the house?

9 How would you describe the conversation between Clara and Freddy? How is it different to Clara's conversation with the young man in the shop?

10 Why do you think Clara changes her mind and eventually agrees to go to the party?

11 What effect does the return of the young man have on Freddy? And on Clara?

12 Why do you think Clara says *Pay any time* when the young man offers to pay for the record?

13 What is Freddy's conversation mainly about in the car? How does Clara respond?

14 How do you think Clara feels about going to the party? What do you think is the significance of the final paragraph?

Character

15 How would you describe Clara? Do you think she will ever be happy?

16 How is Effie different to Clara? What do you think her future will be?

17 Describe the young man who comes to the shop. Do you think that Clara is attracted to him? What is his attitude to Clara?

18 How would you describe Freddy? Which animal does Bates compare him to?
19 Is Freddy believable as a character? How do you feel about the contrast Bates makes between him and the young man?
20 How do you think Clara feels about Freddie? How would you describe her attitude to him?

Narration

21 What do you think Bates's attitude is towards Clara? Do you think he feels sympathy towards her?
22 Is there a good balance in the story between third-person narrative and direct speech? Which do you think predominates?
23 Bates is noted for his naturalistic dialogue. How does he convey the young man's shyness and Clara's response to him?
24 Think about the conversation between Freddie and Clara. Is there real communication between them? How would you describe Freddie's way of talking?
25 Bates often writes about people trapped by circumstances. Do you think he portrays Clara as a victim?

Atmosphere

26 The story takes place at Christmas time. How do you think the people in the story want to feel at this time? Think about Clara, Effie, Freddie and the young man. Do they want different things?
27 How does Bates communicate the restrictions of small-town life? Think about Clara's reflections on the town and her memories of the Williamson's parties.
28 How would you describe the atmosphere of Clara's encounters with the young man? Are they different to the atmosphere of her meeting with Freddie?
29 Find places in the story where Bates describes the landscape around the town. How does he convey its beauty? Are there other moments of beauty in the story?

Style

30 Look at the first two paragraphs of the story. Notice the repetition of *lessons in voice training, won many examinations, one could imagine, dreary.* What effect does this repetition have?

31 Freddy is often compared to a dog: *small poodle-like eyes, lips rather like those of a heavy, wet dog* etc. Find some more examples. What effect do they have?

32 Look at the first conversation between the young man and Clara [pages 133–4]. How many questions does Clara ask? What is the effect of this?

33 Look at the conversation between Clara and Freddy [pages 136–7]. How does Freddy speak? How does Bates convey his character?

34 Look at the passage where Freddy drives Clara to the party [pages 139–40]. Notice how descriptions of the sky or landscape alternate with Freddy's comments. What does this show about Clara's state of mind?

Guidance to the above literary terms, answer keys to all the exercises and activities, plus a wealth of other reading-practice material, can be found on the student's section of the Macmillan Readers website at: www.macmillanenglish.com/readers.

The Sensible Thing
by F Scott Fitzgerald

About the author

Francis Scott Key Fitzgerald was born in 1896 in St Paul, Minnesota in the USA. He is best known for his novels about life in the American 'Jazz Age', the 1920s.

Fitzgerald was encouraged to write by his teachers at school, and he wrote stories for the school magazine. Even at Princeton University, his writing took priority over his studies. He joined the army in 1917, and the following summer, when he was at an army camp in Alabama, he met and fell in love with Zelda Sayre. She was young, beautiful and rich, the 18 year-old daughter of a wealthy family. He desperately wanted to marry her, but Zelda wanted someone who was more successful.

Determined to win her, Fitzgerald worked hard on his first novel, *This Side of Paradise*. It was published in 1920, sold well, and made Fitzgerald rich. Zelda and he got married, and moved to New York where he wrote a second novel, *The Beautiful and Damned*. This was also a success, and the Fitzgeralds began to live a life of luxury and excess. Their daughter Frances was born in 1921.

Both Fitzgerald and Zelda suffered from health problems which were made worse by their heavy drinking. In 1924, when they were living in France, *The Great Gatsby* was published but did not enjoy the same commercial success as his other novels. They moved back to the US where, in 1930, Zelda had a nervous breakdown. Her treatment was expensive; when *Tender is the Night* was published in 1934, Fitzgerald hoped it would pay their debts. It was not a great success, however, and by now Fitzgerald himself was ill.

In 1937, Fitzgerald moved to Hollywood to work as a screenwriter, while Zelda stayed behind. He fell in love with Sheilah Graham, a journalist, and spent the rest of his life with her. Fitzgerald's last novel was *The Last Tycoon*, which was unfinished when he died of a heart attack in 1940. Zelda died in 1948 in a fire at the clinic where she was being treated.

Ironically[1], the novels which were less successful in Fitzgerald's lifetime are now thought to be his best. Several of his books have been made into films, including *The Great Gatsby* and *Tender is the Night*. Apart from his novels, he wrote over one hundred and fifty short stories.

About the story

The Sensible Thing was first published in *Liberty* magazine in 1924. It later appeared in the collection *All the Sad Young Men*. In 1996, it was made into a film for TV.

Background information

The Jazz Age

Fitzgerald is often associated with the term 'The Jazz Age'. It describes the period after the First World War, during the 1920s. Jazz was a popular form of music at the time but 'The Jazz Age' also refers to a time when people wanted to enjoy themselves and forget about their problems. In the social circles of the Fitzgeralds, financial success meant parties and a hectic social life. There was little thought for tomorrow, and some people criticised their lifestyle for its extravagance.

Zelda and Scott

The story reflects many of the elements of Zelda and Fitzgerald's own early relationship. Zelda was from a comfortable, Southern family and had dreams, hopes and plans for her future. She wrote and painted and, in her 20s, made serious attempts to become a ballet dancer. Fitzgerald was desperate to marry her but Zelda wanted someone more successful. It is significant that they married very quickly after Fitzgerald's first novel became a success. They were both young and attractive and became famous for their extravagant and glamorous lifestyle. Things began to go badly wrong when Fitzgerald was no longer financially successful and their lives were marked by debt and bad health.

---

1 used for saying that a situation developed in an unexpected and sometimes humorous way

Summary

It may help you to know something about what happens in the story before you read it. Don't worry, this summary does not tell you how the story ends!

George O'Kelly is a young man who works as an insurance clerk in New York City. Two years earlier, he had a job in Tennessee as a construction engineer and he had great hopes for the future. He went to New York to make money, but things did not go well. Now, he is poor and desperate and living in one room in a horrible apartment.

The person responsible for this situation, as he sees it, is his girlfriend in Tennessee, Jonquil Carey, who has been waiting for George to become successful before she would marry him. She has sent him a letter suggesting that they break off their relationship.

George sends her a telegram saying he will arrive in Tennessee the next day. He asks his manager for some time off. This is the second time he has asked for a holiday in a few weeks and the manager fires him. To his surprise, George thanks him and shakes his hand.

The next day, George's girlfriend meets him at the station. She is there with two boys who drive George to Jonquil's house.

Jonquil's parents ask George about his job and he lies and tells them that he has been promoted and given a better salary.

When they are alone, the subject turns to marriage and George becomes very nervous. He reproaches Jonquil for sending him the letter and she begins to cry.

The next day, the couple's relationship is in crisis because Jonquil has guessed the truth about George. George knows he must leave. Jonquil goes with him to the station where they say goodbye awkwardly.

Fifteen months later, in September, George returns to the city in Tennessee and checks in to a hotel. Since his last visit, he has made great progress and worked as an engineer in Peru and New York. He arranges to visit Jonquil. They go to see a woman who has a beautiful garden full of chrysanthemum flowers. On their return, Jonquil tells George that she will never marry, and he tells her that he must go to Washington to see someone who has been kind to him. He asks her to sit on his knee as she used to, and he tells her about his good fortune in South America.

Pre-reading exercises
Key vocabulary

This section will help you familiarise yourself with some of the more specific vocabulary used in the story. You may want to use it to help you before you start reading, or as a revision exercise after you have finished the story.

Language for describing feelings

For most of the story, George is in a state of tension and anxiety. His only moments of calm are when he is with Jonquil but these too are mixed with his fears of losing her.

---

distraught extremely worried, upset or confused
to brood to think and worry about something a lot
ill-humour *formal* bad mood
overcome adj something overcomes you when it makes you feel very emotional
to blurt (out) to say something suddenly and without thinking about the effect it will have, usually because you are nervous or excited
to jump at conclusions to make a decision about something too quickly without knowing all the facts (usage: it is usual now to say 'jump *to* conclusions')
sorrow great sadness
to falter *mainly literary* if your steps falter, you stop walking
dazed unable to think clearly or understand what is happening because you are surprised or upset
to waver if a person wavers, they are not certain about what to say or do
offhand unfriendly in the way you treat someone
poignant giving you feelings of sadness

---

1 **Answer the questions below.**

a) Which two adjectives describe sadness?
b) Which two verbs describe uncertainty or hesitation?
c) Which two expressions suggest that someone is not thinking clearly?
d) Which adjective do you think describes George when he has to ask his manager for more holiday?

2 **Use a suitable form of one of the words or expressions in the box above to complete these sentences.**

1 He felt .... and regret at causing such great pain.

2 Do you really think they are having an affair just because they were laughing together? Stop .... !

3 Sue was very .... with me this morning. I don't think she wants to see me again.

4 When John saw his girlfriend again after six months, he was .... with happiness.

5 Stop .... about your exams. You'll be fine!

6 Ann hasn't eaten or slept since Max finished with her. She's absolutely ....

7 Without intending to, he .... the truth to his mother.

8 It was very .... to see all the flowers and candles which people had left at the scene of the accident.

9 John was doing so well in business and making great progress. But I think he's .... since his father died.

10 When they received the news, they were initially rather .... and couldn't take everything in.

11 He appeared to be confident, but as he approached, his steps .... and when he eventually spoke his voice .... a little.

12 The children are .... today – they have been fighting all morning.

Formal language

Although the dialogue in the story is mostly clear and colloquial, Fitzgerald sometimes uses formal or literary language in his third-person narrative. Look at the following examples. In a) the author tells us about Jonquil's parents and their attitude to George. In b) we learn about George's career after he leaves Jonquil.

a) *They had been sorry when he had given it up and gone to New York to look for something more immediately profitable, but while they deplored the curtailment of his career they sympathized with him and were ready to recognise the engagement.*

b) *He had made a remarkable showing for a young engineer – stumbled into two unusual opportunities, one in Peru, whence he had just returned and another consequent upon it, in New York, whither he was bound.*

3 Answer the questions below.

a) Which verb means *not to approve of something?*
b) Which noun means *cutting (something) short?*
c) Which adverb means *from where?*
d) Which adverb means *to where?*
e) Which phrase means *as a result?*

Note: *Whence* and *whither* are very old-fashioned words which are usually only used in poetry. You will rarely find them in modern English.

Main themes

Before you read the story, you may want to think about some of its main themes. The questions will help you think about the story as you are reading it for the first time. There is more discussion of the main themes in the *Literary analysis* section after the story.

The American Dream

The term 'American Dream' refers to the ideal of equal opportunity that is associated with the USA. In a young country, made up of immigrants, everyone was, in theory, equal, and anyone could become a success through hard work, and imagination. It was important to earn money for other people to admire you. In the story, George hopes to win the love and approval of Jonquil, and her parents, so he lies about his job and prospects. He later takes advantage of a piece of luck and is able to do really well. Although he wins the girl of his dreams, he feels that he loses something in the process.

4 As you read, ask yourself:

a) How far is George following his own dream and how far is he following the American Dream, imposed by society?
b) Do you think this story could happen today?

Young love

George is a young man who has put love before practical considerations. He has a good job in Tennessee but is impatient to do better, so he goes to New York where he thinks he will rise faster. Things do not work out as he hopes, and he ends up as an insurance clerk earning $40 per week. He blames his girlfriend for his situation, but he also knows that he must do better in life to win her love. He is confused when he meets her: she won't marry him if he can't do better in life, but he thinks he will do better in life if she loves and supports him. At first, they do *the sensible thing* and split up. When his financial circumstances change, Jonquil comes back to him. Fitzgerald's portrayal of the meetings between George and Jonquil show the contradictions and changing emotions of the young couple as they explore their feelings for each other.

5 As you read the story, ask yourself:

a) Does Fitzgerald paint a convincing story of a young man in love?
b) Why/why not?

❦

The Sensible Thing

by F Scott Fitzgerald

1

At the Great American Lunch Hour[2] young George O'Kelly straightened his desk deliberately and with an assumed air of interest. No one in the office must know that he was in a hurry, for success is a matter of atmosphere, and it is not well to advertise the fact that your mind is separated from your work by a distance of seven hundred miles.

But once out of the building he set his teeth and began to run, glancing now and then at the gay[3] noon of early spring which filled Times Square and **loitered** less than twenty feet over the heads of the crowd. The crowd all looked slightly upwards and took deep March breaths, and the sun dazzled their eyes so that scarcely anyone saw anyone else but only their own reflection on the sky.

George O'Kelly, whose mind was over seven hundred miles away, thought that all outdoors was horrible. He rushed into the subway[4], and for ninety-five blocks bent a **frenzied** glance on a car-card[5] which showed vividly how he had only one chance in five of keeping his teeth for ten years. At 137th Street he broke off his study of commercial art[6], left the subway, and began to run again, a tireless, anxious run that brought him this time to his home – one room in a high, horrible apartment-house in the middle of nowhere.

There it was on the bureau, the letter – in **sacred** ink, on blessed[7] paper – all over the city, people, if they listened, could

2 Fitzgerald romanticises the hour most workers have for lunch
3 *old-fashioned*: happy
4 *US*: underground train
5 *old-fashioned, US*: card or poster in the train with an advertisement on it
6 *unusual, phrase 'commercial art'*: visual advertising
7 *mainly literary*: used for emphasizing that something makes you feel happy or grateful because it is just what you need

hear the beating of George O'Kelly's heart. He read the commas, the blots, and the thumb-smudge[8] on the margin – then he threw himself hopelessly upon his bed.

He was in a **mess**, one of those terrific messes which are ordinary incidents in the life of the poor, which follow poverty like birds of prey. The poor go under or go up or go wrong or even go on, somehow, in a way the poor have – but George O'Kelly was so new to poverty that had any one denied the uniqueness of his case he would have been astounded.

Less than two years ago he had been graduated with honours from The Massachusetts Institute of Technology and had taken a position with a firm of construction engineers in southern Tennessee. All his life he had thought in terms of tunnels and skyscrapers and great squat dams and tall, three-towered bridges, that were like dancers holding hands in a row, with heads as tall as cities and skirts of cable strand. It had seemed romantic to George O'Kelly to change the sweep of rivers and the shape of mountains so that life could **flourish** in the old bad lands of the world where it had never taken root before. He loved steel, and there was always steel near him in his dreams, liquid steel, steel in bars, and blocks and beams and formless plastic masses, waiting for him, as paint and canvas to his hand. Steel inexhaustible, to be made lovely and austere in his imaginative fire …

At present he was an insurance clerk at forty dollars a week with his dream slipping fast behind him. The dark little girl who had made this mess, this terrible and **intolerable** mess, was waiting to be sent for in a town in Tennessee.

In fifteen minutes the woman from whom he sublet[9] his room knocked and asked him with maddening kindness if, since he was home, he would have some lunch. He shook his head, but the interruption aroused him, and getting up from the bed he wrote a telegram.

'*Letter depressed me have you lost your nerve you are foolish and*

8 a small, untidy mark made, in this case, by ink on someone's thumb
9 *to let* is to rent; George is renting a flat, house, etc from someone who is renting it from someone else

just upset to think of breaking off why not marry me immediately sure
we can make it all right –'

He hesitated for a wild minute, and then added in a hand[10] that could scarcely be recognized as his own: 'In any case I will arrive tomorrow at six o'clock.'

When he finished he ran out of the apartment and down to the telegraph office near the subway stop. He possessed in this world not quite one hundred dollars, but the letter showed that she was 'nervous;' and this left him no choice. He knew what 'nervous' meant – that she was emotionally depressed, that the prospect of marrying into a life of poverty and struggle was putting too much **strain** upon her love.

George O'Kelly reached the insurance company at his usual run, the run that had become almost second nature to him, that seemed best to express the tension under which he lived. He went straight to the manager's office.

'I want to see you, Mr Chambers,' he announced breathlessly.

'Well?' Two eyes, eyes like winter windows, **glared** at him with ruthless impersonality.

'I want to get four days' vacation.'

'Why, you had a vacation just two weeks ago!' said Mr Chambers in surprise.

'That's true,' admitted the **distraught** young man, 'but now I've got to have another.'

'Where'd you go last time? To your home?'

'No, I went to – a place in Tennessee.'

'Well, where do you want to go this time?'

'Well, this time I want to go to – a place in Tennessee.'

'You're **consistent**, anyhow,' said the manager dryly. 'But I didn't realize you were employed here as a travelling salesman.'

'I'm not,' cried George desperately, 'but I've got to go.'

'All right,' agreed Mr Chambers, 'but you don't have to come back. So don't!'

'I won't.' And to his own **astonishment** as well as Mr Chambers' George's face grew pink with pleasure. He felt happy,

10 *mainly literary:* someone's handwriting

exultant[11] – for the first time in six months he was absolutely free. Tears of gratitude stood in his eyes, and he seized Mr Chambers warmly by the hand.

'I want to thank you,' he said with a rush of emotion, 'I don't want to come back. I think I'd have gone crazy if you'd said that I could come back. Only I couldn't quit[12] myself, you see, and I want to thank you for – for quitting for me.'

He waved his hand magnanimously, shouted aloud, 'You owe me three days' salary but you can keep it!' and rushed from the office. Mr Chambers rang for his stenographer[13] to ask if O'Kelly had seemed queer[14] lately. He had fired many men in the course of his career, and they had taken it in many different ways, but none of them had thanked him – ever before.

2

Jonquil Cary was her name, and to George O'Kelly nothing had ever looked so fresh and pale as her face when she saw him and fled[15] to him **eagerly** along the station platform. Her arms were raised to him, her mouth was half parted for his kiss, when she held him off suddenly and lightly and, with a touch of embarrassment, looked around. Two boys, somewhat younger than George, were standing in the background.

'This is Mr Craddock and Mr Holt,' she announced cheerfully. 'You met them when you were here before.'

Disturbed by the transition of a kiss into an introduction and **suspecting** some hidden significance, George was more confused when he found that the automobile[16] which was to carry them to Jonquil's house belonged to one of the two young men. It seemed to put him at a disadvantage. On the way Jonquil chattered between the front and back seats, and when he tried to slip his arm around her under cover of the twilight[17] she **compelled** him

11 *literary:* very pleased and excited, especially about something you have achieved
12 *US, colloquial:* resign from your job
13 *old-fashioned:* someone whose job it is to take notes (usually in a court setting using a special machine)
14 *old-fashioned:* strange
15 *old-fashioned, literary:* to run away; to escape from a dangerous situation or place very quickly
16 *old-fashioned:* a car
17 *mainly literary:* the time in the evening when the sky is beginning to turn dark

with a quick movement to take her hand instead.

'Is this street on the way to your house?' he whispered. 'I don't recognize it.'

'It's the new boulevard[18]. Jerry just got this car today, and he wants to show it to me before he takes us home.'

When, after twenty minutes, they were deposited at Jonquil's house, George felt that the first happiness of the meeting, the joy he had recognized so surely in her eyes back in the station, had been **dissipated** by the intrusion of the ride. Something that he had looked forward to had been rather **casually** lost, and he was brooding on this as he said good night stiffly to the two young men. Then his ill-humour faded as Jonquil drew him into a familiar embrace under the dim light of the front hall and told him in a dozen ways, of which the best was without words, how she had missed him. Her emotion reassured him, promised his anxious heart that everything would be all right.

They sat together on the sofa, overcome by each other's presence, beyond all except fragmentary[19] endearments[20]. At the supper hour Jonquil's father and mother appeared and were glad to see George. They liked him, and had been interested in his engineering career when he had first come to Tennessee over a year before. They had been sorry when he had given it up and gone to New York to look for something more immediately profitable, but while they deplored[21] the curtailment[22] of his career they sympathized with him and were ready to recognize the engagement. During dinner they asked about his progress in New York.

'Everything's going fine,' he told them with enthusiasm. 'I've been promoted – better salary.'

He was miserable as he said this – but they were all *so* glad.

'They must like you,' said Mrs Cary, 'that's certain – or they wouldn't let you off twice in three weeks to come down here.'

18 a wide road in a town or city often with trees along it
19 made up of a lot of separate pieces that are not connected
20 *formal, literary:* a word or phrase that you say to someone you love
21 *formal:* to dislike something very much, often because you think it is immoral
22 *formal:* reduction or limiting

'I told them they had to,' explained George hastily[23]; 'I told them if they didn't I wouldn't work for them any more.'

'But you ought to save your money,' Mrs Cary reproached him gently. 'Not spend it all on this expensive trip.'

Dinner was over – he and Jonquil were alone and she came back into his arms.

'So glad you're here,' she sighed. 'Wish you never were going away again, darling.'

'Do you miss me?'

'Oh, so much, so much.'

'Do you – do other men come to see you often? Like those two kids?'

The question surprised her. The dark **velvet** eyes stared at him.

'Why, of course they do. All the time. Why – I've told you in letters that they did, dearest.'

This was true – when he had first come to the city there had been already a dozen boys around her, responding to her **picturesque** fragility[24] with adolescent worship, and a few of them perceiving that her beautiful eyes were also sane and kind.

'Do you expect me never to go anywhere' – Jonquil demanded, leaning back against the sofa-pillows until she seemed to look at him from many miles away – 'and just fold my hands and sit still – forever?'

'What do you mean?' he blurted out in a panic. 'Do you mean you think I'll never have enough money to marry you?'

'Oh, don't jump at conclusions so, George.'

'I'm not jumping at conclusions. That's what you said.'

George decided suddenly that he was on dangerous grounds. He had not intended to let anything spoil this night. He tried to take her again in his arms, but she resisted unexpectedly, saying:

'It's hot. I'm going to get the electric fan[25].'

23 done in a hurry, without carefully planning or thought
24 something that is easy to break or damage
25 a machine with blades that turns and moves the air in the room to make it less hot, powered by electricity

When the fan was adjusted they sat down again, but he was in a supersensitive mood and **involuntarily** he plunged into the specific world he had intended to avoid.

'When will you marry me?'

'Are you ready for me to marry you?'

All at once his nerves gave way, and he sprang to his feet.

'Let's shut off that damned[26] fan,' he cried, 'it drives me wild. It's like a clock ticking away all the time I'll be with you. I came here to be happy and forget everything about New York and time –'

He sank down on the sofa as suddenly as he had risen. Jonquil turned off the fan, and drawing[27] his head down into her **lap** began **stroking** his hair.

'Let's sit like this,' she said softly, 'just sit quiet like this, and I'll put you to sleep. You're all tired and nervous and your sweetheart'll take care of you.'

'But I don't want to sit like this,' he complained, **jerking** up suddenly, 'I don't want to sit like this at all. I want you to kiss me. That's the only thing that makes me rest. And any ways I'm not nervous – it's you that's nervous. I'm not nervous at all.'

To prove that he wasn't nervous he left the couch and plumped himself into a rocking-chair across the room.

'Just when I'm ready to marry you you write me the most nervous letters, as if you're going to **back out**, and I have to come rushing down here –'

'You don't have to come if you don't want to.'

'But I *do* want to!' insisted George.

It seemed to him that he was being very cool and logical and that she was putting him deliberately in the wrong. With every word they were drawing farther and farther apart – and he was unable to stop himself or to keep worry and pain out of his voice.

But in a minute Jonquil began to cry sorrowfully and he came back to the sofa and put his arm around her. He was the comforter

26 *impolite:* used to say that you don't care at all about someone or something
27 *formal, unusual use:* move slowly, smoothly

now, drawing her head close to his shoulder, murmuring[28] old familiar things until she grew calmer and only trembled a little, spasmodically[29], in his arms. For over an hour they sat there, while the evening pianos thumped their last cadences[30] into the street outside. George did not move, or think, or hope, lulled into numbness[31] by the **premonition** of disaster. The clock would tick on, past eleven, past twelve, and then Mrs Cary would call down gently over the banister[32] – beyond that he saw only tomorrow and despair.

3

In the heat of the next day the breaking-point came. They had each guessed the truth about the other, but of the two she was the more ready to admit the situation.

'There's no use going on,' she said miserably, 'you know you hate the insurance business, and you'll never do well in it.'

'That's not it,' he insisted **stubbornly**; 'I hate going on alone. If you'll marry me and come with me and take a chance with me, I can make good at anything, but not while I'm worrying about you down here.'

She was silent a long time before she answered, not thinking – for she had seen the end – but only waiting, because she knew that every word would seem more cruel than the last. Finally she spoke:

'George, I love you with all my heart, and I don't see how I can ever love anyone else but you. If you'd been ready for me two months ago I'd have married you – now I can't because it doesn't seem to be the sensible thing.'

He made wild accusations – there was someone else – she was keeping something from him!

'No, there's no one else.'

This was true. But reacting from the strain of this affair she

28 say something in a quiet voice
29 happening for short periods
30 *literary:* the way in which a person's voice gets louder or softer as they speak
31 *mainly literary:* the condition of not being able to feel part of your body
32 a structure like a fence along the edge of a stair, designed to keep you from falling off the edge

had found relief in the company of young boys like Jerry Holt, who had the merit of meaning absolutely nothing in her life.

George didn't take the situation well, at all. He seized her in his arms and tried literally to kiss her into marrying him at once. When this failed, he broke into a long monologue[33] of self-pity, and ceased only when he saw that he was making himself despicable[34] in her sight. He threatened to leave when he had no intention of leaving, and refused to go when she told him that, after all, it was best that he should.

For a while she was sorry, then for another while she was merely kind.

'You'd better go now,' she cried at last, so loud that Mrs Cary came downstairs in alarm.

'Is something the matter?'

'I'm going away, Mrs Cary,' said George brokenly. Jonquil had left the room.

'Don't feel so badly, George.' Mrs Cary blinked at him in helpless sympathy – sorry and, in the same breath, glad that the little tragedy was almost done. 'If I were you I'd go home to your mother for a week or so. Perhaps after all this is the sensible thing – '

'Please don't talk,' he cried. 'Please don't say anything to me now!'

Jonquil came into the room again, her sorrow and her nervousness alike tucked under powder and rouge[35] and hat.

'I've ordered a taxicab,' she said impersonally. 'We can drive around until your train leaves.'

She walked out on the front porch[36]. George put on his coat and hat and stood for a minute exhausted in the hall – he had eaten scarcely a bite since he had left New York. Mrs Cary came over, drew his head down and kissed him on the cheek, and he felt very ridiculous and weak in his knowledge that the scene had been ridiculous and weak at the end. If he had only gone the

33 a long speech by one speaker; someone who doesn't let others speak in a conversation
34 *formal, old-fashioned:* extremely unpleasant
35 make up for the face
36 a small area covered by a roof at the entrance to a house or other building

night before – left her for the last time with a decent pride.

The taxi had come, and for an hour these two that had been lovers rode along the less-frequented streets. He held her hand and grew calmer in the sunshine, seeing too late that there had been nothing all along to do or say.

'I'll come back.' He told her.

'I know you will,' she answered, trying to put a **cheery** faith into her voice. 'And we'll write each other – sometimes.'

'No,' he said, 'we won't write. I couldn't stand that. Some day I'll come back.'

'I'll never foret you, George.'

They reached the station, and she went with him while he bought his ticket…

'Why, George O'Kelly and Jonquil Cary!'

It was a man and a girl whom George had known when he had worked in town, and Jonquil seemed to greet their presence with relief. For an interminable[37] five minutes they all stood there talking; then the train roared into the station, and with ill-concealed **agony** in his face George held out his arms towards Jonquil. She took an uncertain step toward him, faltered, and then pressed his hand quickly as if she were taking leave of a chance friend.

'Good-bye, George,' she was saying. 'I hope you have a pleasant trip.'

'Good-bye, George. Come back and see us all again.'

Dumb, almost blind with pain, he seized his suitcase, and in some dazed way got himself aboard the train.

Past clanging[38] street-crossings, gathering speed through wide suburban spaces towards the sunset. Perhaps she too would see the sunset and pause for a moment, turning, remembering, before he faded with her sleep into the past. This night's **dusk** would cover up forever the sun and the trees and the flowers and laughter of his young world.

---

37 *mainly literary:* continuing for a long time in a boring or annoying way
38 the sound made by something made of metal hitting other metal

4

On a damp afternoon in September of the following year a young man with his face burned to a deep copper glow got off a train at a city in Tennessee. He looked around anxiously, and seemed relieved when he found that there was no one in the station to meet him. He taxied to the best hotel in the city where he registered with some satisfaction as George Kelly, Cuzco, Peru.

Up in his room he sat for a few minutes at the window looking down into the familiar street below. Then with his hand trembling faintly he took off the telephone receiver and called a number.

'Is Miss Jonquil in?'

'This is she.'

'Oh –' his voice after overcoming a faint tendency to waver went on with friendly formality.

'This is George Kelly. Did you get my letter?'

'Yes. I thought you'd be in today.'

Her voice, cool and unmoved, disturbed him, but not as he had expected. This was the voice of a stranger, unexcited, pleasantly glad to see him – that was all. He wanted to put down the telephone and catch his breath.

'I haven't seen you for – a long time.' He succeeded in making this sound **offhand**. 'Over a year.'

He knew how long it had been – to the day.

'It'll be awfully nice to talk to you again.'

'I'll be there in about an hour.'

He hung up. For four long seasons every minute of his leisure had been crowded with anticipation of this hour, and now this hour was here. He had thought of finding her married, engaged, in love – he had not thought she would be unstirred[39] at his return.

There would never again in his life, he felt, be another ten months like these he had just gone through. He had made an admittedly remarkable showing[40] for a young engineer –

39 *old-fashioned, literary:* not emotionally affected
40 amount of success someone has during a period of time

stumbled into two unusual opportunities, one in Peru, whence[41] he had just returned, and another consequent upon it[42], in New York, whither[43] he was bound[44]. In this short time he had risen from poverty into a position of unlimited opportunity.

He looked at himself in the dressing-table mirror. He was almost black with **tan**, but it was a romantic black, and in the last week, since he had had time to think it, it had given him considerable pleasure. The hardiness[45] of his frame[46], too, he appraised[47] with a sort of fascination. He had lost part of an eyebrow somewhere, and he still wore an elastic bandage on his knee, but he was too young not to realise that on the steamer many women had looked at him with unusual tributary[48] interest.

His clothes, of course, were frightful[49]. They had been made for him by a Greek tailor in Lima – in two days. He was young enough, too, to have explained this sartorial[50] deficiency[51] to Jonquil in his otherwise laconic[52] note. The only further detail it contained was a request that he should *not* be met at the station.

George O'Kelly, of Cuzco, Peru, waited an hour and a half in the hotel, until, to be exact, the sun had reached a midway position in the sky. Then, freshly shaven and talcum-powdered[53] towards a somewhat more Caucasian hue[54], for vanity at the last minute had overcome romance, he engaged a taxicab and set out for the house he knew so well.

41 *literary, out of use:* from where
42 happening as a result of something
43 *old-fashioned, literary, out of use:* to where
44 *old-fashioned, literary:* going
45 *US:* strength and ability to deal with or exist in unpleasant or extreme conditions
46 *mainly literary:* the particular size and shape of someone's body
47 *formal:* to evaluate
48 *formal, unusual:* paid as a tribute; showing respect and admiration
49 *informal, old-fashioned:* extremely serious or unpleasant
50 relating to clothes or how they are made
51 a lack of something
52 *mainly literary:* using very few words
53 covered in talcum powder – a soft white powder that you sometimes put on your body after taking a bath or shower
54 used to describe the colour (hue) of a white person, indigenous European

He was breathing hard – he noticed this but he told himself that it was excitement, not emotion. He was here; she was not married – that was enough. He was not even sure what he had to say to her. But this was the moment of his life that he felt he could least easily have dispensed with. There was no triumph, after all, without a girl concerned, and if he did not lay his spoils at her feet[55] he could at least hold them for a passing moment before her eyes.

The house loomed up suddenly beside him, and his first thought was that it had assumed a strange unreality. There was nothing changed – only everything was changed. It was smaller and it seemed shabbier than before – there was no cloud of magic **hovering** over its roof and issuing from the windows of the upper floor. He rang the doorbell and an unfamiliar coloured[56] maid appeared. Miss Jonquil would be down in a moment. He wet his lips nervously and walked into the sitting-room – and the feeling of unreality increased. After all, he saw, this was only a room, and not the enchanted[57] chamber where he had passed those **poignant** hours. He sat in a chair, amazed to find it a chair, realizing that his imagination had **distorted** and coloured all these simple familiar things.

Then the door opened and Jonquil came into the room – and it was as though everything in it suddenly blurred before his eyes. He had not remembered how beautiful she was, and he felt his face grow pale and his voice diminish to a poor sigh in his throat.

She was dressed in pale green, and a gold ribbon bound[58] back her dark, straight hair like a crown. The familiar velvet eyes caught his as she came through the door, and a spasm of fright went through him at her beauty's power of inflicting pain.

He said 'Hello', and they each took a few steps forward and shook hands. Then they sat in chairs quite far apart and gazed at

55 *phrase, old-fashioned, mainly literary:* 'to lay your spoils at someone's feet'– to show someone the benefits you have earned or something you have won
56 *out of use, offensive:* referring to a person who has one parent or grandparent who is white and one who is not
57 *literary:* affected by special magic powers
58 tied

each other across the room.

'You've come back,' she said, and he answered just as **tritely**: 'I wanted to stop in and see you as I came through.'

He tried to neutralize[59] the tremor in his voice by looking anywhere but at her face. The obligation to speak was on him, but, unless he immediately began to **boast**, it seemed that there was nothing to say. There had never been anything casual in their previous relations – it didn't seem possible that people in this position would talk about the weather.

'This is ridiculous,' he broke out in sudden embarrassment. 'I don't know exactly what to do. Does my being here bother you?'

'No.' The answer was both reticent and impersonally sad. It depressed him.

'Are you engaged?' he demanded.

'No.'

'Are you in love with someone?'

She shook her head.

'Oh.' He leaned back in his chair. Another subject seemed exhausted – the interview was not taking the course he had intended.

'Jonquil.' He began, this time on a softer key, 'after all that's happened between us. I wanted to come back and see you. Whatever I do in the future I'll never love another girl as I've loved you.'

This was one of the speeches he had rehearsed. On the steamer[60] it had seemed to have just the right note – a reference to the tenderness he would always feel for her combined with a **non-committal** attitude towards his present state of mind. Here with the past around him, beside him, growing minute by minute more heavy on the air, it seemed **theatrical** and stale.

She made no comment, sat without moving, her eyes fixed on him with an expression that might have meant everything or nothing.

59 to stop something from having any effect
60 US: a large boat that moves by using steam which pushes a set of paddles joined together in the shape of a large wheel

'You don't love me any more, do you?' he asked her in a level voice.

'No.'

When Mrs Cary came in a minute later, and spoke to him about his success – there had been a half-column about him in the local paper – he was a mixture of emotions. He knew now that he still wanted this girl, and he knew that the past sometimes comes back – that was all. For the rest he must be strong and watchful and he would see.

'And now,' Mrs Cary was saying, 'I want you two to go and see the lady who has the chrysanthemums[61]. She particularly told me she wanted to see you because she'd read about you in the paper.'

They went to see the lady with the chrysanthemums. They walked along the street, and he recognized with a sort of excitement just how her shorter footsteps always fell in between his own. The lady turned out to be nice, and the chrysanthemums were enormous and extraordinarily beautiful. The lady's gardens were full of them, white and pink and yellow, so that to be among them was a trip back into the heart of summer. There were two gardens full, and a gate between them; when they **strolled** towards the second garden the lady went first through the gate.

And then a curious thing happened. George stepped aside to let Jonquil pass, but instead of going through she stood still and stared at him for a minute. It was not so much the look, which was not a smile, as it was the moment of silence. They saw each other's eyes, and both took a short, faintly accelerated breath, and then they went on into the second garden. That was all.

The afternoon **waned**. They thanked the lady and walked home slowly, thoughtfully, side by side. Through dinner, too, they were silent. George told Mr Cary something of what had happened in South America, and managed to let it be known that everything would be **plain sailing** for him in the future.

Then dinner was over, and he and Jonquil were alone in the room which had seen the beginning of their love affair and the

61 a plant with large, round, brightly-coloured flowers

end. It seemed to him long ago and inexpressibly sad. On the sofa he had felt agony and grief such as he would never feel again. He would never be so weak or so tired and miserable and poor. Yet he knew that that boy of fifteen months before had had something, a trust, a warmth that was gone forever. The sensible thing – they had done the sensible thing. He had **traded** his youth for strength and carved success out of despair. But with his youth, life had carried away the freshness of his love.

'You won't marry me, will you?' he said quietly.

Jonquil shook her dark head.

'I'm never going to marry,' she answered.

He nodded.

'I'm going to Washington in the morning,' he said.

'Oh –'

'I have to go. I've got to be in New York by the first, and meanwhile I want to stop off in Washington.'

'Business!'

'No-o,' he said as if reluctantly. 'There's someone there I must see who was very kind to me when I was so – down and out[62].'

This was invented. There was no one in Washington for him to see – but he was watching Jonquil narrowly, and he was sure that she **winced** a little, that her eyes closed and then opened wide again.

'But before I go I want to tell you the things that happened to me since I saw you, and, as maybe we won't meet again, I wonder if – if just this once you'd sit in my lap like you used to. I wouldn't ask except since there's no one else – yet – perhaps it doesn't matter.'

She nodded, and in a moment was sitting in his lap as she had sat so often in that **vanished** spring. The feel of her head against his shoulder, of her familiar body, sent a shock of emotion over him. His arms holding her had a tendency to tighten around her, so he leaned back and began to talk thoughtfully into the air.

He told her of a despairing two weeks in New York which had terminated with an attractive if not very profitable job in a construction plant in Jersey City. When the Peru business

62 US: very poor with nowhere to live and no job

had first presented itself it had not seemed an extraordinary opportunity. He was to be third assistant engineer on the expedition, but only ten of the American party, including eight rodmen and surveyors[63], had ever reached Cuzco. Ten days later the chief of the expedition was dead of yellow fever. That had been his chance, a chance for anybody but a fool, a marvellous chance –

'A chance for anybody but a fool?' she interrupted innocently.

'Even for a fool,' he continued. 'It was wonderful. Well. I wired[64] New York –'

'And so,' she interrupted again, 'they wired that you ought to take a chance?'

'Ought to!' he exclaimed, still leaning back. 'That I *had* to. There was no time to lose – '

'Not a minute?'

'Not a minute.'

'Not even time for – ' she paused.

'For what?'

'Look.'

He bent his head forward suddenly, and she drew herself to him in the same moment, her lips half open like a flower.

'Yes,' he whispered into her lips. 'There's all the time in the world...'

All the time in the world – his life and hers. But for an instant as he kissed her he knew that though he search through eternity he could never recapture those lost April hours. He might press her close now till the muscles knotted on his arms – she was something desirable and rare that he had fought for and made his own – but never again an **intangible** whisper in the dusk, or on the breeze of night …

Well, let it pass, he thought; April is over, April is over. There are all kinds of love in the world, but never the same love twice.

63 someone whose job is to measure areas of land in order to make maps
64 *US*: to send a telegram to someone

Post-reading exercises

Understanding the story

1 **Use these questions to help you check that you have understood the story.**

Part 1

1 Where is George at the beginning of the story? What time of day is it?
2 Why does George go home?
3 What did George study and what is he doing now?
4 Why does George go to the telegraph office?
5 What happens when George asks the manager for some time off?

Part 2

6 Where does Jonquil meet George?
7 Who takes George to Jonquil's house?
8 What does George tell Jonquil's parents about his job?
9 Why is George nervous when he is alone with Jonquil?

Part 3

10 What happens the next day between George and Jonquil?
11 Who do they meet at the station? What effect does this have?

Part 4

12 When does George next return to Tennessee? Where has he been during the previous months?
13 What impression does George have of Jonquil's house?
14 How does Jonquil affect George when he sees her?
15 Why do they go to see the *lady with the chrysanthemums*? What is the *curious thing* that happens there?
16 What reason does George give Jonquil for going to Washington?
17 What does George talk about when Jonquil is sitting on his lap?
18 How does George feel when he realises that Jonquil is now his?

Language study

Grammar

Similes

A simile is a comparison between one thing and another, of a different kind. Similes are usually introduced with the word *like*.

1 Look at these similes from the story. Match the two parts of the sentences or phrases.

one of those terrific messes …	*like a flower*
tall, three-towered bridges	*ticking away all the time I'll be with you*
Two eyes, eyes	*which follow poverty like birds of prey*
It's like a clock	*like winter windows*
her lips half open	*that were like dancers holding hands in a row*

In your opinion…
a) Which simile describes George's manager?
b) Which describes the beginning of a kiss?
c) Which expresses George's irritation with the noise of an electric fan?
d) Which describes George's romantic feelings towards engineering?
e) Which describes George's situation at the beginning of the story?

Conditionals

There are many uses of conditional sentences in the story. They are not always expressed with *if* and they do not always follow the conventional pattern of first, second and third conditionals, as presented in many grammar books. Here are some sentences that follow a more conventional pattern:

I think I'd have gone crazy if you'd said that I could come back. (third conditional: George speaking to the manager)
If you'd been ready for me two months ago, I'd have married you. (third conditional: Jonquil speaking to George)
If I were you, I'd go home to your mother for a week or so. (second conditional: Mrs Cary speaking to George)

The following sentence seems to break the 'rule' about the first conditional (If + present tense, followed by will + verb in the second clause), but is in fact a common example of a 'mixed' conditional.

> If you'll marry me and come with me and take a chance with me, I can make good at anything (George speaking to Jonquil)

Literary conditionals

In a literary style, if is sometimes omitted and structures such as had, should and were + pronoun are used. For example:

> George O'Kelly was so new to poverty that **had** anyone denied the uniqueness of his case he would have been astounded

If only

If only is used (usually with a past or past perfect tense) to express a strong wish or regret:

> **If** he had **only** gone the night before – left her for the last time with a decent pride.

Though

Fitzgerald uses though instead of if or even if in this sentence – another example of a literary use of the conditional.

> … he knew that **though** he search through eternity he could never recapture those lost April hours

2   **Write these examples of literary conditionals in a more conventional way. We have done the first one for you, as an example.**

1   Had I known he was going to visit, I would have worn something smarter.
If I had known he was going to visit, I would have worn something smarter.

2   Though I were offered a fortune, I would not go there again.

3   Were he to ask her to marry him, she would probably accept.

4   Should the theatre be full, let me know.

5 She was so lonely, that had he asked her out she would definitely have gone.

6 What would you do should he break off the engagement?

7 Search for years though you may, you will never find another man like him.

8 Had she realised the extent of the problem, she would have intervened sooner.

Adverbs of manner

Fitzgerald uses a great variety of adverbs of manner in the story to describe actions and develop his characters. Most adverbs of manner answer the question *How?* and are often formed by adding *–ly* to an adjective. Another way of describing actions is by using a prepositional phrase which may or may not contain an adverb, for example, *with enthusiasm, in surprise, with barely concealed anger*.

3 Answer the questions below.

a) Which are the adverbs of manner in the phrases below?
b) Which are prepositional phrases?
c) Which adverb does not end in *–ly*?

> 1 *she held him off suddenly and lightly*
> 2 *he threw himself hopelessly upon his bed*
> 3 *he bent his head forward suddenly*
> 4 *with a rush of emotion*
> 5 *she began to cry sorrowfully*
> 6 *they walked home slowly, thoughtfully*
> 7 *with ruthless impersonality*
> 8 *watching Jonquil narrowly*
> 9 *He was breathing hard*
> 10 *wet his lips nervously*

4 Adverbs of manner are often used after verbs such as *say,*
explain, insist, etc. Look at the following examples from the text.
Underline the verb and adverb.

> she announced cheerfully
> he said goodnight stiffly
> he said as if reluctantly
> he explained hastily
> he insisted stubbornly
> he answered just as tritely
> she interrupted innocently
> said George brokenly

5 Make adverbs from the adjectives in brackets and write them in
the correct place in the sentence. We have done the first one for
you.

1 'Goodnight,' she said and closed the door. (angry, hard)
   'Goodnight,' she said angrily, and closed the door hard.

2 He answered her question before anyone else had the chance to
   interrupt. (quick)

3 'I suppose we should leave soon,' said Ellen. (reluctant)

4 On the night of the concert, the stars shone and she played the
   piano. (bright, perfect)

5 With his hand trembling, he gave her the ring. (faint)

6 Her voice went on and the students fought to stay awake.
   (monotonous)

7 The train stopped, and then pulled out of the station. (brief)

8 'Put the car away, will you?' he shouted. (rude)

9 The little boy jumped off the diving board. (enthusiastic)

10 The man pressed her hand and strolled away. (intimate)

Literary analysis

Plot

1 **Do you agree or disagree with these sentences about the plot? If you disagree, explain why.**

1 It is obvious from the beginning, that George is not interested in his job in the office.

2 He is in a hurry to get home because he wants to read again the letter that Jonquil has written to him.

3 George has a dream that he will change the world through his knowledge of insurance.

4 George is making progress in achieving his ambitions.

5 George's manager is surprised after he fires George.

6 George is pleased to see Jonquil and her two friends.

7 It is possible that Mrs Cary knows that George is lying to her.

8 Both Jonquil and George are upset at the end of their first evening together.

9 It is George who ends the relationship with Jonquil.

10 George gets a better job as a result of his success in Peru.

11 George decides he still wants Jonquil after she tells him she loves him.

12 Something significant happens at the chrysanthemum gardens.

13 Jonquil may be affected by jealousy towards the end of the story.

14 George is not in love with Jonquil at the end of the story.

Character

15 How would you describe George at the beginning of the story? Why does he run everywhere?

16 How would you describe George at the end of the story? Has he changed?

17 What is your impression of Jonquil? Think of some words to describe her.

18 What is your impression of Jonquil's parents, especially Mrs Cary?

19 Are George and Jonquil in love with each other? Do you think one of them is more in love than the other?

Narration

20 The story is written from George's point of view but in the third person. This enables the author to comment objectively on:

George's situation: eg George O'Kelly, *whose mind was over seven hundred miles away ... ; It had seemed romantic to George O'Kelly to change the sweep of rivers ...*

Why does Fitzgerald use George's full name? What effect do comments like this have?

21 Look at this extract from the story:

> *The sensible thing – they had done the sensible thing. He had traded his youth for strength and carved success out of despair. But, with his youth, life had carried away the freshness of his love.*

How far do you think this is Fitzgerald's own opinion? Is he exaggerating?

22 Look at the final paragraph of the story. Is it similar to the extract above? Do you think Fitzgerald is trying to make a moral point in the last sentence? If so, what is it?

23 Where do you think Fitzgerald's sympathies lie: with George, with Jonquil, or with both? What is his attitude to their conversation and behaviour?

Atmosphere

24 How does the author convey George's mood of desperation in Part 1 of the story?

25 What is the atmosphere like between George and Jonquil when he first visits Tennessee? How does Fitzgerald convey this? Think of their conversation, his use of adjectives and adverbs.

26 How does the atmosphere change when George visits Tennessee in Part 4 of the story?

27 Choose two or three more words to add to the suggestions below, to describe the atmosphere of the story:
Part 1: *agitation*,
Part 2: *conflict*,
Part 3: *despair*,
Part 4: *acceptance*,

Style

28 Fitzgerald sometimes writes in a lyrical style that reflects the heightened emotions and aspirations of his young hero. Look at the episode describing the sun in Time Square, and the episode about George's dreams of being an engineer. How would you

describe these episodes? Can you think of any more in the story?

29 Fitzgerald can be quite humorous at times. Examples are the reference to The Great American Lunch Hour, his observation that *success is a matter of atmosphere*, George's study of the car-card on the subway and the conversation with the manager. What makes these episodes amusing?

30 One of the ways in which Fitzgerald creates humour is to abruptly change his style and move, for example, from lyrical to practical, from long sentences to short, from dreams to reality. An example of this is the description of George's dreams followed by a short statement of his actual situation [page 155]. Can you think of any other examples of this technique?

31 Fitzgerald often uses repetition of words or phrases. Find these examples in the story. What effect do they have?

... it is not well to advertise the fact that your mind is separated from your work by a distance of seven hundred miles.

George O'Kelly, whose mind was over seven hundred miles away ...

The poor go under or go up or go wrong or even go on, somehow, in a way the poor have ...

He loved steel ... always steel near him in his dreams, liquid steel, steel in bars and blocks ...

Guidance to the above literary terms, answer keys to all the exercises and activities, plus a wealth of other reading-practice material, can be found on the student's section of the Macmillan Readers website at: www.macmillanenglish.com/readers.

Essay questions

Language analysis

Discuss how one of the language areas you have studied contributes to the telling of two of the stories in the collection.

Analysing the question

What is the question asking?

It is asking you to:
- choose one language area from the index
- explain how this language area functions in the context of storytelling
- use examples from two or more of the stories in the collection.

Preparing your answer

1 Look back through the *Language analysis* sections of the stories you've read and choose a language area that you feel confident about.
2 Make notes about the language area. Include notes on form, function and use.
3 Choose examples from two stories. Choose examples from both classic and contemporary stories, if possible.
4 Look back at the question and your notes and plan your essay. Use the structure of the question to structure your essay. Here is an example:

Introduction	Introduce the area you are going to describe.
Main body 1	Explain the general function of the area you have chosen; use examples from both stories.
Main body 2	Analyse how the area contributes to the style and atmosphere of both stories, referring to specific passages in the stories.
Conclusion	Summarise the literary use and function of the language area you focused on.

Literary analysis

Compare and contrast the attitude to romantic relationships of the main characters in two of the stories.

Analysing the question

What is the question asking?

It is asking you to:
- look at two stories in the collection
- describe the attitude to romantic relationships of the main character in each story
- describe any similarities and differences.

Preparing your answer

1 Choose two stories with two characters that are different enough to allow you to contrast them.
2 Make notes about the characters: what they are like and how they feel about love and romantic relationships.
3 Find key scenes in the stories where the characters' attitudes are described or expressed through speech. Make a note of any useful quotations.
4 Make a list of similarities and differences between the characters; think of the setting, the social background and when the story was written.
5 Read the question again and write a plan for your essay. Here is an example:

Introduction	Briefly introduce the two stories.
Story 1	Describe the first story and its main character.
Story 2	Describe the second story and its main character.
Similarities	Discuss the similarities.
Differences	Discuss the differences.
Conclusion	Make a general comment about attitudes to romantic relationships as described in love stories.

For tips on writing academic essays, and essays about literary analysis, visit the student's section of the Macmillan Readers' website at www.macmillanenglish.com/readers.

Glossary

The definitions in the glossary refer to the meanings of the words and phrases as they are used in the short stories in this collection. Some words and phrases may also have other meanings which are not given here. The definitions are arranged in the story they appear, and in alphabetical order.

Second Best

as a rule PHRASE usually

baffled (adj) confused, not understanding

cluster (n) a small close group of something

complexion (n) the appearance of the skin on someone's face and whether it is pale, dark, smooth etc

corpse (n) the body of a dead person

drain (n) a very small amount of water

fidget (v) to touch or move something with your fingers because you are bored, nervous or concentrating on something else

flare (n) a bright flame that burns for a short time

grope (v) to search for something you cannot see, using your hands

hitch (v) to pull something you are wearing to a higher position

husk (n) the dry outer cover of grain

jar (v) to find unpleasant or unsuitable

keen (adj) very strong

knitting (to knit) her brows
  PHRASE moving your eyebrows close together in an expression that shows that you are feeling worried or serious, or are thinking carefully about something

matter-of-fact (adj) showing no emotion when dealing with something upsetting, exciting etc.

mole (n) a small animal with dark fur that lives in the ground

mow (v) to cut grass

muse (v) to think about something in a careful, slow way

nuisance (n) something that is annoying and a continuing problem

obtuse (adj) someone who is obtuse does not understand explanations or situations quickly

paddle (v) to swim slowly by moving your arms and legs gently through the water

peculiar (adj) strange, often in an unpleasant way

quiver (a) a slight shaking movement or sound

reckless (adj) not thinking about the possible bad effects of your actions

row to move a boat through water using long flat poles (oars)

scruff (n) back (of the neck)

shaft (n) a long, narrow passage

shift (v) to move your body slightly

shuffle (v) to walk slowly and carefully without lifting your feet

sickly (adj) a smell that is so unpleasant it makes you feel sick

single file (n) a line of people or things in which one is directly behind another

snappy (adj) trying to bite or snap; a snappy person speaks to people in a quick, angry way

snout (n) the long nose of an animal

spark (n) a small, burning particle

spasmodic (adj) happening for short periods and not often

stealthy (adj) quiet and still so that no-one sees you

struggle (v) to try hard to do something that you find difficult

suffocate (v) to feel very uncomfortable because there is not much fresh air to breathe; to die because you cannot breathe

teens (n) the years of your life between the age of 13 and 19; 'in her/his teens'

tilt (v) to move something so that one side is lower than the other

vicious (adj) extremely unkind or unpleasant

whimsical (adj) made or done for fun, not seriously

wrestle (v) to fight by trying to throw your opponent to the ground

wretch (n) someone in a bad situation that you feel sorry for or dislike

wriggle (v) to move by twisting and turning quickly

writhe (v) to move by twisting and turning, especially when you feel a lot of pain

Bliss

absurd (adj) completely stupid, unreasonable or impossible to believe

acute (adj) very serious or severe

anguish (n) a feeling of great physical or emotional pain

ardent (adj) feeling or showing a particular emotion very strongly

bizarre (adj) strange and difficult to explain

bliss (n) complete happiness

charming (adj) very attractive and pleasant

chilly (adj) cold enough to be unpleasant

couch (n) a long, low comfortable seat that two or three people can sit on

creepy (adj) causing an unpleasant feeling of fear or unease

crouch (v) to move your body close to the ground by bending your knees and leaning forward slightly

crumble (v) to break something into very small pieces (noun – 'crumbs' – small pieces)

divine (adj) extremely good or pleasant; like a god or relating to God

dizzy (adj) feeling as if you or the things around you are spinning, especially when you think you are going to fall

dreadful (adj) very unpleasant

extravagant (adj) spending or costing a lot of money, especially when it is unreasonable

far-fetched (adj) difficult to believe because it is very unlikely

flick (n) a sudden quick movement

float (v) to be lighter than air, and move slowly through it

fluke (n) something that happens unexpectedly because of an accident or good luck

frank (adj) honest about the situation and your opinions, even if this offends people

glide (v) to move in a smooth and easy way with no noise

grin (n) a big smile that shows your teeth

hideous (adj) very ugly or frightening in appearance

hug (v) to put your arms round someone to show your love or friendship

idiotic (adj) extremely stupid

impulsive (adj) someone who is impulsive tends to do things without thinking about what will happen as a result

infallible (adj) not capable of making mistakes

in (full) bloom (adjectival phrase) if a tree or a plant is in bloom it is covered in flowers

miraculous (adj) extremely lucky and unexpected

offend (adj) to make someone upset or angry by doing or saying something

petal (n) one of the coloured parts around the centre of a flower

precious (adj) worth a lot of money; loved or valued by someone

provoke (v) to deliberately try to make someone angry

pyramid (n) a large stone structure with a square base and walls with three sides that meet at a point at the top of the structure. The most famous ones were built in ancient Egypt

radiant (adj) very bright, extremely happy

rank (taxi rank) (n) a place where customers wait for taxis

rattle (v) if something rattles, it makes short, sharp knocking sounds as it moves or shakes

ridiculous (adj) silly or unreasonable and deserving to be laughed at

rim (n) the edge of an open container or circular object

rustle (v) to make a sound like the one that leaves or sheets of paper make when they move

scheme (n) an idea, plan or a system

seldom (adj) not often; 'rarely'

slender (adj) tall or long or thin in an attractive manner

sound (adj) reliable and sensible

squeeze (v) to press something firmly, especially with your hands

swarm (verb) the movement of a cloud of flying insects

teeming with (adj) containing or consisting of an extremely large number of people, animals or objects that are moving around

transparent (adj) clear or thin enough to see through

tug (v) to pull someone or something by making a short, strong movement

unbearable (adj) so extreme that you cannot deal with the pain, feeling; similar to 'intolerable'

victim (n) someone who has been harmed, injured or killed as the result of a crime

weep (v) to cry because you feel unhappy or because you have some other strong emotion

A Shocking Accident

abrupt (adj) sudden and unexpected, often in an unpleasant way

anecdote (n) a story you tell people about something interesting or funny that happened to you

appease (v) to give your opponents what they want

apprehensive (adj) slightly worried or nervous

at a loss (to do something) confused and not knowing what to do

as a last resort used to say that you will do something only after trying everything else to solve a problem

become (verb) if something becomes you, it is suitable for you or makes you more attractive

blackmail (n) the crime of making someone give you money to do what you want by threatening to tell people embarrassing information about them

brood (v) to think and worry about something a lot

callousness (n) feeling no emotion when you see people in trouble or in pain

civilized (adj) society/country which has developed an advanced culture or institutions; polite and reasonable

commiseration (n) sympathy for someone who is unhappy about something

convulsion (noun) violent movements of a person's body that they cannot control

discourse (noun) long and serious speech or piece of writing on a particular subject

distinguished (adj) successful and respected by many people

expel (verb) to officially force someone to leave a place or organization because of bad behaviour

flag (verb) to become tired or weak

glazed (adj) a glazed expression shows that someone is not at all interested in something

intrinsically (adj) relating to the essential features or qualities of something

masterly (adj) done in a very skilful and clever way

obscurity (noun) a state in which a person or thing is not known or not remembered

pompous (adj) self-important, speaking in a way which is very serious and formal

rambling (adj) long and confusing

ricochet (v) if a moving object ricochets, it hits a surface at an angle and immediately moves away from it at a different angle

The Jilting of Jane

agreeable (adj) pleasant, nice or satisfactory

anticipate (verb)

apprentice (noun) someone who works for a particular person or company, usually for low pay, to learn the type of work they do

apropos (prep) relating to

brittle (adj) hard and easily broken

cab (n) taxi

clergyman (n) a man who leads religious services

complacent (adj) too confident and relaxed because you think you can deal with something easily, even though this may not be true

cry (your / her / his) heart out
PHRASAL VERB to cry in an uncontrolled way

crushingly (adv) in a very critical and severe way

culmination (n) final result of a process or situation

dilated (adj) if part of your body dilates, it becomes bigger and wider

dismay (n) a feeling of being very worried, disappointed or sad about something

dustpan (n) a small, flat container that you put on the floor and brush dust into

etiquette (n) a set of rules for behaving correctly in social situations

fit (n) a strong, emotional reaction that you cannot control

flit (v) to move quickly from one place to another

flushed (adj) looking red because you are hot, ill, angry or excited

flutter (v) move with short, quick, light movements

fume (v) to feel or show a lot of anger

grasp (v) to understand

grave (adj) looking very serious and worried

heave a sigh PHRASE to let out a deep breath, for example because you are upset or pleased about something

mince (v) to cut meat into very small pieces

moth (n) an insect like a butterfly that comes out mainly at night

orphan (n) a child whose parents have died

parody (noun) a literary or musical work that copies a serious work in a humorous way

porter (n) someone whose job is to carry things or help people with their bags

reluctant (adj) not willing to do something

run (verb) to control or organise

saturated (adj) full of, obsessed

scrub (v) to wash or clean something by rubbing it hard, especially with a brush

shabby (adj) old and in bad condition

silk (n) thin, smooth cloth made from fibres produced by an insect called the silk worm

startled (adj) suddenly frightened or surprised by something

A Christmas Song

bay window (n) a large window that sticks out from the main wall of a house

brittle (adj) hard and easily broken into pieces

carol (n) a traditional song sung at Christmas

clumsy (adj) not careful or graceful, breaking things and knocking against them

dreary (adj) making you feel bored or unhappy

fidget (v) to keep making small, quick movements with parts of your body because you are bored, nervous or impatient

fumble (verb) to try to hold, move or find something, using your hands in a way that is not skilful or graceful

gauze (n) thin white material with holes often used for making curtains

gay (old-fashioned) happy and excited

get away with something
PHRASAL VERB to manage to do something bad without being punished or criticized for it

glittering (adj) bright and shining with a lot of quick flashes of light

grind (v) to press something down onto a surface using a lot of force

haste (n) great speed in doing something because of limited time

hearty (adj) friendly, loud and over-enthusiastic

infectious (adj) an infectious disease is one that can spread from one person to another

meagre (adj) smaller, or less than you want or need

rowdy (adj) noisy and causing trouble

ruffle (v) to touch someone's hair in a friendly way

seize (v) to suddenly and firmly hold someone by a part of their body or clothing

shriek (n) a high, loud shot of excitement, surprise or fear

sulky (adj) feeling angry or unhappy and not wanting to talk to anyone or be with other people

transfigure (verb) to change the appearance of someone or something, especially in a way that makes them look more beautiful

The SensibleThing

agony (n) great pain

back out (v) to decide not to do something that you agree to do

boast (v) to proudly tell people about what you have or do in order to make them admire you

casual (adj) relaxed, informal

cheery (adj) feeling or showing happiness

compel (v) to force someone to do something

consistent (adj) not changing in behaviour, qualities or attitude

dazzle (v) to blind with strong light

dissipate (v) to make something gradually disappear

distort (v) to change something such as information so that it is no longer true or accurate

distraught (adj) extremely worried, upset or confused

dumb (adj) *(mainly American) stupid; (old-fashioned)* unable to speak (in modern English 'speech impaired')

dusk (n) the period of time at the end of the day just before it becomes dark

eagerly (adv) to do something with enthusiasm

flee (v) to run away

flourish (v) to grow well and be healthy

frenzied (adj) done in an extremely uncontrolled way, often by someone who is crazy

glare (v) to look at something or someone in a very angry way

hover (v) to stay in the same position in the air

intangible (adj) not able to be touched or measured

intolerable (adj) impossible to bear or deal with

involuntary (adj) an involuntary movement, sound or reaction is one made suddenly in a way that cannot be controlled

jerk (v) to move suddenly

lap (n) the top half of your legs above your knees when you sit down

loiter (v) to stay somewhere longer than you should or is normal

mess (n) a difficult situation with a lot of problems, especially when people have made mistakes

non-committal (adj) not saying what you think or what you plan to do

offhand (adj) unfriendly in the way you treat someone

plain sailing something easy to do or achieve

picturesque (adj) attractive, especially if it is old or interesting

poignant (adj) giving you feelings of sadness

premonition (n) a strong feeling that something is going to happen, especially something bad

sacred (adj) holy or connected with God in a special way

sane (adj) able to think and speak in a reasonable way and to behave normally

strain (n) mental pressure or worry

stroke (v) to gently move your hand over skin, fur or hair

stroll (v) to walk without hurrying, often for pleasure

stubborn (adj) not willing to change your ideas or consider anyone else's reasons or arguments

suspect (v/n) to believe that something is true, especially something bad

tan (n) a light brown colour (often used to refer to skin – a suntan)

theatrical (adj) relating to the business or art of the theatre; theatrical behaviour is very emotional and aims to attract attention

trade (v) to exchange

trite (adj) not interesting or original because it is what people usually say in a particular situation

vanished (adj) disappeared, no longer there

velvet (n) cloth that is very soft on one side and very smooth on the other

wane (v) to become weaker or less important

wince (v) to react to something with a sudden expression on your face that shows you are embarrassed or feel pain

Dictionary extracts adapted from the Macmillan English Dictionary © Macmillan Publishers Limited 2002

Language study index

For more information and free resources visit:
www.macmillanenglish.com/readers

MACMILLAN READERS